THE
GOSPEL
ACCORDING
TO
BUBBA

CHUCK MEYER

Illustrations by
Cindy Mayfield and Donna Utsler

Stone Angel Books
Austin, Texas

For
my parents, Carl and Martha Meyer,
good Episcopalians of Ohio
who finally understood the move to Texas;
my brother Bud and his wife Joanne,
who will move here shortly;
and my wife, Debi, who had the good sense
to be born to Ben and Annette Ludeman
in the South Texas town of Cotulla
And for Michal Leah our daughter
who, like me, is Texan not by birth but by soul.

Introduction

In order to appreciate the stories in this book there are some things you need to know, otherwise you will find yourself flipping back and forth, wondering if you read a previous piece correctly. In one conversation you will find the author single, while at another point having a daughter; at one point his wife, Deb, has died, and at another his wife Debi is very much alive, and the mother of said daughter. All of the above is true, you just have to get the sequence straight.

The stories told here cover a long span of time during which my life changed dramatically. I went from being married with no children to being a widower, to being married with a six year old daughter as a part of the bargain. The one constant during this extended period filled with ups and downs, with tragedy and joy, with failure and success, was my angel-friend Bubba.

Originally appearing when I was married, Bubba provided my first wife, Deb, with moments of consternation and laughter. When she died, he proved to be consoling but also questioning and cajoling, ultimately demanding that we wrestle (as he claims he did with

Jacob) until newness emerged. Six years of singlehood later, when I married Debi, even the kid-fearing Bubba was smitten with daughter Michal Leah, and he began telling stories with children and (saints preserve us) *cats* in them. Heaven (and Bubba) only knows where we will venture together from here.

Thanks are due to Cindy Mayfield and Donna Utsler, the Austin artists who are responsible for the "drawin's" in this volume. Their endurance with my constant requests for just one more sketch by an unreasonable deadline is surpassed only by their patience with getting Bubba to sit still after jogging to pose.

Kim Campbell, my friend and co-worker at St. David's Medical Center, follows her successful design of the cover on my last book, The Eighth Day, with the even more vibrant cover of this book. Bubba and I will be pleased some day to say we knew her back before she was famous.

Thoroughly Thoughtful Debi Meyer, Gail Roberts The Arthritis Nurse, and Eagle Eye Picky Velma Brady proofed the original and made comments that were usually helpful and sometimes (on Debi's part anyway) embarrassingly accurate. Bubba reminds me that I am supposed to be grateful for their suggestions, so I am.

Finally, someone obviously afflicted with terminal seriosity suggested that the cover include the admonition: "WARNING: THE THEOLOGY CONTAINED

IN THIS VOLUME MAY BE HAZARDOUS TO YOUR RELIGION."

Bubba and I certainly hope so.

Stories

Foreword

"I first met Bubba in 1977, shortly after I moved to Texas. I was scheduled to do a service at St. David's Episcopal Church in Austin and the text was a difficult one."

"Hold on, son. Yore gettin' it all messed up. Let me tell the story."

"Bubba! This is my book and my introduction to it. So buzz off and..."

"Wrong again, boy. You need my help with this, you just don't know it yet. And I also been meanin' to tell you about that title you wrote. It's awful. It'll never fly, so to speak."

"What's wrong with it? *Conversations With A Lone Star Celestial Being* is an excellent title. It describes the main thrust of the book and..."

"The *MAIN* thrust? Boy, don't you know the *MAIN* thrust in this book is *ME*."

"Your modesty is underwhelming, Bubba. Nevertheless, the main thrust of each story is a thorough explication of the Biblical text. The stories talk about real people doing real things. They talk about common, ordinary people encountering a God who reaches out to them. They talk about..."

"They talk about you and me drinkin' Shiner Beer."

"Bubba!"

"Well, they *do*!

"Well, we do! And so do a lot of people when they're sharing their stories. Especially the kind of stories you tell."

"They ain't exactly stories, you know. They're just kind of variations on what happened. And, of course, they're all true."

"I know - or so you tell me. The hard part was writing them all down right after you left each time, since your voice won't come out on a tape recorder. Isn't that sort of like a vampire?"

"Watch it now, son," Bubba smirked. "Next thing you know, people will think you been *channelin'* or somethin'. Course that might be an improvement on some o' them E-piscopal sermons I've heard."

"Bubba!"

"Now you know I'm right, boy. I swear I think they teach you to sterilize yore sermons before you give 'em. I mean, y'all give some real snoozers. Yours, though, *are* different."

"Thanks, Bubba."

"Course that's 'cause *you've* got ME."

"If I agree with you will you go away and let me write this introduction?"

"Not unless you agree to put my name in the title. I mean, let's give credit where credit's due."

"Bubba, you're being unreasonable. What am I going to call it: LONE STAR ANGEL?"

"Now, don't go gettin' a burr under yore saddle, boy. I'm just askin' for a little piece of the title, a little somethin' that mentions my part in puttin' this book together, a small indication that I had somethin' to do with it."

"I have this strange feeling that you already have something in mind."

"Ya might say that."

"Oh no. What is it?"

"Ya really want to hear it?"

"Do I have a choice?"

"No."

"Then go for it."

"How 'bout: THE GOSPEL ACCORDING TO BUBBA?"

"How about go mind your own business and leave this decision to me?"

"Okay. Okay. I can take a hint. But before I go let me ask you one question."

"What's that?"

"Do you want people to READ this stuff? I mean, do you actually want these stories sittin' in people's livin' rooms for strangers to browse through and enjoy some of the talks we've had?"

"Of course I do, Bubba."

"Then which title do you think people will pick off the bookshelf to read through - some dry old worn out name like you want, or an interestin', appealin', smart, catchy title like mine?"

"I see your point."

"Course you do, son. Yore problem is you keep forgettin' who the *angel* is around here."

"Alright. Suppose I do change it to *THE GOSPEL ACCORDING TO BUBBA*? So now will you fly off into the night and let me finish this? I was about to describe how we met before you appeared out of nowhere."

"That's mainly why I showed up, son. I wanted to make sure you got the story straight and I was just positive as a polecat you'd tell it wrong."

"What's to tell wrong? I was dealing with a difficult piece of scripture. I didn't quite know how to go about telling about it and suddenly this six foot, slightly overweight being, dressed in a fringed Western suit with boots and a cowboy hat appears at my front door with some story about a wing out of place...."

"See? I knew you'd get it all backwards. What happened is I was flyin' over Austin, doin' my rounds, when I overheard you moanin' and groanin' about that Bible passage. The Boss made it clear at our angels convention that He was gettin' a tad hacked at some of the pablum preachin' down there lately so I decided to pay you a visit. The old 'wing story' gets me in every time. I knew you needed help and, since I was in the neighborhood anyway...."

"And since you knew I had some cold Shiner Bock on hand..."

"Well, I knew that wouldn't hurt either. The point is you needed help and I was thirsty. So we bartered. I told you what to say and you offered me a bit of Texas hospitality."

"And a strange and wonderful relationship was begun."

"That's right, son. You're strange and I'm wonderful."

"Bubba!"

"Just joshin' with ya, boy. Actually, I even like the way you wrote these stories. I think humans will appreciate 'em too, even if they are a mite on the Texan side. And if they don't...well, shoot-fire, boy, we'll just *secede*."

"Speaking of seceding, don't you have someplace else to go now that you've named the book and written the foreword?"

"Come to think of it I do, son. I got to fly on down to the St. David's Hospital Gift Shop and get me a new pen and..."

"What do you need a pen for?"

"Son, when this book gets out just who do you think people are gonna want at the autograph parties - *you*?"

"Well, I was kind of hoping..."

"Yeah, come to think of it I guess they might let you be there too. And I do have to get this cleared with the Boss, ya know. Cain't make public appearances without the Boss's okay."

"And what if the Boss...I mean what if God says 'No?'"

"Then you'll just to have to sign my 'X' for me."

"Your 'X'? You mean....you mean you can't write your name?"

"Good grief, son! Do I have to remind you again yore talkin' to a' angel here? If I wrote my name not only could you not *read* it - you couldn't even *spell* it. Half the heavenly host have trouble pronouncin' it!"

"Then how about if I just sign it 'Bubba'?"

"As in *THE GOSPEL ACCORDING TO...?*"

"Yes, as in *THE GOSPEL ACCORDING TO....*"

"That'd be just fine, boy."

"Then bye, Bubba."

"Bye, son. And keep the Shiner cold for me. I'll be back."

"I'm sure you will, Bubba. I'll even look forward to it. Sort of."

Austin, Texas
September, 1992

Ecclesiasticus 15.11-20

Do not say, 'The Lord was responsible for my sinning,'
    for he is never the cause of what he hates.
Do not say, 'It was he who led me astray,'
    for he has no use for a sinner.
The Lord hates all that is foul,
    and no one who fears him will love it either.
He himself made man in the beginning,
    and then left him free to make his own decisions.
If you wish, you can keep the commandments;
    to behave faithfully is within your power.
He has set fire and water before you;
    put out your hand to whichever you prefer.
    Man has life and death before him;
    whichever a man likes better will be given him.
For vast is the wisdom of the Lord;
    he is almighty and all-seeing.
His eyes are on those who fear him,
    he notes every action of man.
He never commanded anyone to be godless,
    he has given no one permission to sin.

Matthew 5.21-24, 27-30, 33-37

"You have heard that it was said to the men of old, 'You shall not kill; and whoever kills shall be liable to judgment.' But I say to you that everyone who is angry with his brother shall be liable to judgment; whoever insults his brother shall be liable to the council, and whoever says 'You fool!' shall be liable to the hell of fire. So if you are offering your gift at the altar, and there remember that your brother has something against you, leave your gift there before the altar and go; first be reconciled to your brother, and then come and offer your gift.

"You have heard that it was said, 'You shall not commit adultery.' But I say to you that every one who looks at a woman lustfully has already committed adultery with her in his heart. If your right eye causes you to sin, pluck it out and throw it away; it is better that you lose one of your members than that your whole body be thrown into hell. And if your right hand causes you to sin, cut it off and throw it away; it is better that you lose one of your members than that your whole body go into hell.

"Again you have heard that it was said to the men of old, 'You shall not swear falsely, but shall perform to the Lord what you have sworn.' But I say to you, Do not swear at all, either by heaven, for it is the throne of God, or by the earth, for it is his footstool, or by Jerusalem, for it is the city of the great King. And do not swear by your head, for you cannot make one hair white or black. Let what you say be simply 'Yes' or 'No'; anything more than this comes from evil."

An Angel Named Bubba

For about a year I had been plagued with writing on Scriptures that had to do with hellfire and damnation. Then I finally was presented with an Ecclesiasticus passage that was so delightful I wished I had written it myself. In fact, I was so shaken by it, I had great difficulty developing something to write about.

I sat at my word processor with a disgusted look on my face when there came a knock at the front door. I went to answer it and found a tall, overweight being dressed in orange holding what looked like a large, injured wing.

"Uh, can I help you?" I said.

"I shore hope so, pardner, I shore hope so. Ya see, I'm an angel...."

"A WHAT? I asked.

"An angel, son, an angel. Ain't ya never read yore Bible? You know - Cherubim, Seraphim, Archangels, Los Angeles and like that?"

"Well, yes, but..."

3

"Well, I'm one of 'em and I'm in a peck o' trouble."

"Oh, well, come right in, Mr.....Mr...."

"Just call me 'Bubba,' son; all the heavenly chorus does."

"Certainly, Mr. Bubba, sir, uh, angel, sir," I mumbled with difficulty. "Come right in."

"Thank ya kindly, son."

We walked into the living room and sat down in front of the fireplace.

"Now, as I was sayin.' I'm in a peck of trouble. Ya see, I was on my way to our local angel convention here in Austin, *above* Austin, actually - that reminds me, son, it's gettin' awful crowded up there. Have to move the conventions up some every year. First these bank towers and now more hotels..."

"Tell me about it..."

"Anyway, I was goin' to the convention and this fog came over everything. I got lost comin' over Highway 183 and flew a bit too low. Seem to have sprained my wing on your fence out there."

"Oh, I get it, Bubba. You're sort of an 'angel flying too close to the ground'..."

"That's right, son, that's right. Now if you'll just let me rest a bit here in front of yore fireplace, I think this here wing'll snap back into place in no time. If it don't, I may have to ask you to drive me downtown."

"Fine, Bubba," I said, going to the kitchen. "Can I get you anything to drink? Perrier water? Orange juice?"

"Yuck, son. You *are* Episcopalian, aren'tcha?"

"Yes."

"And this *is* Texas, ain't it?"

"Last time I checked..."

"Well, get out the Shiner beer, then. It's been a rough night and I ain't up for no Baptist soft drinks."

I brought out the drinks and set them in front of him.

"Can I ask you a question...uh...Bubba?"

"You just did, son! You just did! Ask away!"

"Okay. Why are you dressed in orange?"

"You kiddin' me? My territory's central Texas, son. This here's Longhorn Country." He lowered his voice and glanced around as he leaned forward. "But don't tell nobody - I sometimes dress up in Aggie colors, or even SMU or Rice colors. Sorta depends on where I'm at - and what outfit, uh, *fits* me at the time. I like to be flexible. But enough about me, son. I understand you're in a little trouble yourself."

"Say what...?"

"The story yore writin,' boy! The *story*!"

"But, how'd you know about..?"

"Part of the job, boy. I get *paid* for knowin.' Now maybe I could help you out a little bit on it."

"That'd be terrific. Here, let me pour you another one."

I refilled our glasses.

"Now," I said, "...there's this terrific Ecclesiasticus passage..."

"Ah, yes, I remember old Cleesie well. He was a good ol' boy, he was. Wrote some nice stuff."

"Well, what can I say about the passage for today?"

"You can tell folks to stop that old Flip Wilson theology."

"Huh?"

"You know: 'The Devil Made Me Do It.' All that stuff about blamin' their plight on the Devil or on God."

"You mean God doesn't *make* me do things?"

"Read the book, boy, read the book! God created people in the beginning and left them in the power of their own inclinations. If you will, Cleesie says, you can keep the commandments. To act faithfully is a matter of yore own *choice*. Choice is where it's at, boy. People choose how they feel and how they act and how they think. Nobody does that for them - although they sure like to make it look that way."

"Nobody makes anybody else angry or frustrated?"

"'Course not, son. Any self respecting angel knows that. You're in charge of your feelings, It's *yore* choice how you dole 'em out. So stop blamin' God for your problems. God doesn't *make* things happen. God may *permit* them, but God sure ain't into makin' 'em. Tell 'em that, boy. The Boss takes a lot of gas for stuff he ain't had nothin' to do with. The choices are *yours*, son!"

"That implies a lot of responsibility though, Bubba. And you know how we humans don't want to take responsibility for our behavior. It's a lot easier to blame somebody else or to dump it on God. I hear that a lot at the hospital."

"Sure ya do, son. The Boss' been gettin' blamed for illness and death ever since that Job deal. I told the Boss not to get into that, much less let it be written down in that Bible book."

"Yea, Bubba. I hear people talking every day about God *taking* someone when they die."

"God don't *take* nobody, boy! Tell 'em that. The Boss ain't goin' around *snatchin' up* people. God *accepts* them with open arms when their bodies quit workin,' but He don't *take* nobody! There you go again, blamin' the Boss for somethin'."

"But to believe that we have choice in our lives is scary, Bubba. That means we have a lot more power than we let ourselves know."

"That's right, son. Yore catchin' on! The Boss sets before you the circumstances, the choice of fire or water as ol' Cleesie said. You can take as much as you want of either. Enough fire to warm you or to burn you to a crisp. Enough water to quench your thirst - fill 'em up again, son - or enough to drown you. The choice is up to you."

"But where does God come in?"

"The Boss comes in whenever you *call*, boy! God'll help you make the choices and support you and accept you and love you and forgive you when you try to grab too much of the fire or the water - when you try to be *more* than human or *less* than human."

"So it's up to us to choose life or death too?"

"Shore 'nuff! Look around you, son. Lookit all them people smokin' and drinkin' (present company excepted, of course) and runnin' their lives crazy and stressin' themselves out. Course it's their choice and yore's too, I might add."

"And my responsibility. That's the tough part."

"No. I think the responsibility's the *easy* part."

"Huh?"

"I think the tough part's that people don't want to accept the power."

"Same thing, Bubba. We don't want the power because of the responsibility. We'd rather dump it off on God, or the Devil, or the Rector, or the president, or our spouse or whoever. It's a lot easier than taking responsibility for ourselves. And besides that, sometimes it seems too hard to live up to some of the stuff I hear in church."

"Why, boy?"

"Well, take this Jesus passage for instance. I mean, doesn't that imply nobody should get angry, or think lustful thoughts or whatever?"

"Not at all boy, not at all! Just the opposite!"

"What?"

"When Jesus said that if you even *think* of anger or *look* lustfully at someone, he was showin' up that gaggle of bozos known as the Pharisees. They kept the law and felt pretty darned good about it...self righteous, you might say. And now Jesus is sayin' that while they kept the *letter* of the law, they're just like the rest of us in their hearts! He's not sayin' to *never* get angry; in fact, Jesus is sayin' EVERYBODY gets angry, and EVERYBODY has lustful thoughts. That's part of what it means to be human bein's and not God, boy!"

"But if we're imperfect, Bubba, what about that cutting off arms and plucking our eyes out stuff?"

"That just means this is serious business, son. It means that people are responsible for their own behavior, feelings and thoughts...that nobody will answer for *yore* acts but *you*, boy. So you can choose whichever way you want to go. Just don't be upset when the consequences of yore behavior come back to have *eternal* implications."

"So each one of us has power over our own lives, but not over anyone else's. And our natural state is imperfect and our choices have eternal consequences. Sounds very optimistic."

"Not *optimistic* at all, boy. It's *hopeful*. There's a big difference between optimism and Christian hope. Optimism means that everything's fine, that everybody's perfect, that there won't be any problems or mistakes. Christian hope is realistic, son. It includes imperfection and forgiveness and acceptance and love that heals and renews, that returns sight to yore blindness and sets free the part of you that you so tightly bind up in yore everyday life. Tell 'em that, boy, right before they take Communion, tell 'em that."

"How come?"

"Because that's what you're celebrating in the bread and wine, son! Choice, responsibility, forgiveness, renewal and healing."

"Now *that's* exciting!"

"And hopeful, boy. Not optimistic, but hopeful."

He looked at the sundial on his wrist.

"Holy jumpin' Jeremiah! I got to get goin.' Thanks for the drinks. They sure helped warm me up some, just like yore fireplace did."

He adjusted his wing and snapped it back into place.

"Yessir! There it is, good as new. I ought to take up chiropractic!"

"You want me to drive you downtown?

"You kiddin' son? I'm doin' fine. Got just a few minutes to make the openin' speech. But I'll get there."

"Just don't get picked up on a FWI."

"FWI?"

"'Flying While Intoxicated.'"

"Not me, son. I'm fine. Kept to my limit. But I do appreciate you checkin.' Friends don't let angels fly drunk! Neither do Episcopalians. Hey...wait a minute...oh rats..."

"What's the matter?"

"I forgot. The Baptists are sponsoring it this year so..."

He walked back in the living room and picked up the carton of Shiner.

"...Mind if I take the rest of this along to help out the Episcopalians?"

"Help them out?"

"Yeah. They'll need a little help from some holy spirits by the time this convention's over. We're takin' up the ordination of women to the angelhood."

"Sure, take it."

He walked out the door.

"Well, nice meetin' you, boy. I hope our paths cross again sometime."

"Well, leave me if you need to. I will still remember...Bubba flyin' too close to the ground..."

"That'd make a nice song, boy. Maybe I'll ask someone like Willie Nelson to sing it."

He took off into the night.

"Bye, son. Now you be sure and tell 'em all I told you!"

And so I did. And that is why I'm exercising my choice to take no responsibility for this story.

Acts 2.1-21

When the day of Pentecost had come, they were all together in one place. And suddenly a sound came from heaven like the rush of a mighty wind, and it filled all the house where they were sitting. And there appeared to them tongues as of fire, distributed and resting on each one of them. And they were all filled with the Holy Spirit and began to speak in other tongues, as the Spirit gave them utterance.

Now there were dwelling in Jerusalem devout men from every nation under heaven. And at this sound the multitude came together, and they were bewildered, because each one heard them speaking in his own language. And they were amazed and wondered, saying, "Are not all these who are speaking Galileans? And how is it that we hear, each of us in his own native language? Parthians and Medes and Elamites and residents of Mesopotamia, Judea and Cappadocia, Pontus and Asia, Phrygia and Pamphylia, Egypt and the parts of Libya belonging to Cyrene, and visitors from Rome, both Jews and proselytes, Cretans and Arabians, we hear them telling in our own tongues the mighty works of God." And all were amazed and perplexed, saying to one another, "What does this mean?" But others mocking said, "They are filled with new wine."

But Peter, standing with the eleven, lifted up his voice and addressed them, "Men of Judea and all who dwell in Jerusalem, let this be known to you, and give ear to my words. For these men are not drunk, as you suppose, since it is only the third hour of the day; but this is what was spoken by the prophet Joel:

'And in the last days it shall be, God declares.
that I will pour out my Spirit upon all flesh,
and your sons and your daughters shall prophesy,
and your young men shall see visions,
and your old men shall dream dreams;
yea, and on my menservants and my maidservants in
    those days
I will pour out my Spirit; and they shall prophesy.
And I will show wonders in the heaven above
and signs on the earth beneath,
blood, and fire, and vapor of smoke;
the sun shall be turned into darkness
and the moon into blood,
before the day of the Lord comes,
the great and manifest day.
And it shall be that whoever calls on the name of
    the Lord shall be saved.'

John 14.15-17

"If you love me, you will keep my commandments.
And I will pray the Father, and he will give you another
Counselor, to be with you for ever, even the Spirit of
truth, whom the world cannot receive, because it neither
sees him nor knows him; you know him, for he dwells
with you, and will be in you."

The Return of Bubba

A few months ago I was struggling with a story about Ecclesiasticus when there appeared at my door a Texas angel named Bubba. He was about 6'4", had a dislocated wing, and needed to stop in for a drink and some rest before heading on to his angel's convention over Austin.

The last time I saw him he was flying off with the last of the Shiner beer. I assumed that would be the only time I'd hear from him. But then, last night, as I was sitting down at the typewriter to write this story - there came a knock at the door.

I went to answer it and, lo and behold, there stood Bubba, all smiley and holding an ice cold six pack of Shiner Bock.

"Well, don't just stand there with yore face hangin' out, boy. Let me in!" he said.

"BUBBA!" I exclaimed. "What in the name of..."

"Watch yore language, boy."

"What in the world are you doing here?"

"That's just what God said to Elijah, son. But my

14

answer's a little bit different. I just happened to be passin' over the neighborhood and remembered a little debt I owed ya." He handed me the pack. "Here it is. The debt's repaid."

"Why thanks, but you didn't have to..."

"I know I didn't, boy. But we angels have a certain code, ya know."

"A code?"

"Yeah. That thing about doin' to others what you want done to you and like that."

"Well, thanks anyway."

"You're welcome." He sort of rocked on his boots a bit. "Well, since you aren't gonna offer me any of it I guess I'll be..."

"Oh! Excuse me! Sorry, Bubba! I wasn't thinking! Come right in! I've been working on this story for Pentecost, and..."

"PENTECOST!! Holy Toledo! I nearly forgot about that. Why, that's one of my favo-rite celebrations."

"Good, because I've got some questions about it. Sit down and we'll talk about it, if you can spare the time."

"Time? What's time, boy? I've got an eternity." He sat his large frame on the couch. "Where's the glasses?"

"Here," I said, getting out the small glasses we liked. I poured.

"Got any chips, son?"

"Only health food around here, Bubba."

"Got any vegetarian chips, son?"

"Here's some yogurt and seaweed chips. That ought to hold you."

"Thanks a heap. Sorta looks like cow chips. Okay now - what did you want to know about Pentecost?"

"Were you there?"

"Was I there? Was I *there* ? Is the Pope Catholic? Do birds fly? Does a bear have fleas? Of *course* I was there. And a great day it was, too. Timed to coincide with the Jewish celebration of the day the Law was given to Moses - seven weeks after Passover, fifty days after Easter."

"I've heard people call it the birthday of the church."

"Well, people ought to be careful what they call it. People get that all messed up. It *wasn't* the birthday of the church, boy! Less'n you spell church with a large C. When people hear it's the birthday of the church, they think of a denomination or a buildin.' Jesus didn't come to start no denominations or buildin's, boy. That's what the Holy Spirit's all about. Just like Peter said - God poured the Holy Spirit out on ALL flesh, to ALL people. He didn't divide 'em up into Baptists and Muslims and Methodists and Jews and like that - and 'specially not to Episcopalians."

"Yeah. I caught on to that much. And there's no discrimination between young and old, or men and women either, according to the passage. It says *whoever* calls on the name of the Lord will be saved. Is that right?"

"That's right."

"That's too bad."

"Too bad - what's too bad about it, boy?"

"Well, that means the spirit is available even to people I don't like very much or don't understand, or disagree with."

"You got the idea, son!"

"Even to outcasts and people on death row, and Republicans and Democrats and Socialists?"

"Yep."

"Oh, okay. I don't much like it, but okay." I poured us another round. "So, what actually happened back on that day?"

"Just like the book says, boy. Ain'tcha read it?"

"Sure I have. I..."

"Then you tell me."

"It says a bunch of the disciples were in one place and the Holy Spirit filled them and they spoke in different tongues and languages so that they were heard by people from all over the known world."

"Yep. That was basically it."

"So what happened?"

"Blew 'em away, boy! Absolutely blew 'em away! Ya see, they thought that the spirit of God could and would only act through the established religion of the time, and here was God bustin' out all over and in people and through people that were *outside* the establishment!"

"Sounds like we could learn something from that today, Bubba."

"Sure could, son. The church (small c) is gettin' too mainline and established in the culture. Sometimes you cain't tell the church from the society any more. Not at all like back then."

"What do you mean?"

"Hand me another of them yogurt chips and I'll tell ya." I handed him the bowl. He took a handful and chomped them down. "Back then they thought those Christians were nuts, ya know what I mean, boy? I mean bazonkers, one brick short of a load, not playin' with a full deck, not wrapped too tight, their computer was missin' a chip. At Pentecost people thought they were drunk on new wine. Speakin' of which, my glass is empty, boy. You need to learn ya some about hostin' ya know? Anyway, where was I...?"

"You were one brick short of a load."

"Yeah, like I was sayin,' back then Christians were different from the culture, always gettin' into some kind of trouble for not goin' along with the society program of buildin' nukes, or cuttin' back on Social Security or subsidizin' tobacco growers or somethin' like that."

"Oh, I see. So people *outside* the established church today who are protesting and witnessing to the Holy Spirit and experimenting with new structures - that's where the Spirit's moving also?"

"That's right, boy! Now you're catchin' on! The established church is just that - established! Oh, for the good old days when we were a bunch of social outcasts."

"Well, what about people's reactions back then? The Bible in Acts says they were bewildered and amazed and perplexed."

"Sure they were, boy. Here was God doin' somethin' *new* through people that *weren't part of the church!*"

"No wonder they were perplexed then. Here they thought they were doing everything religiously and piously to please God and here was God saying 'I won't be bound by your religiosity - my spirit goes out to ALL who want it.'"

"That's right, boy. Write that down. It's a snappy one-liner."

"Hey, Bubba! I can't write that."

"Why not, boy?"

"It'll scare the living bejeebers out of them."

"What will?"

"Well, look at what's going on here - as if you didn't know already. God takes the initiative and is willing to *come* to us where we are, to *come* to us and to *speak* our language - whatever that language may be - so that we can hear His word to us. I mean, God doesn't demand that we speak *God's* language."

"Couldn't even if you tried, son..."

"That's what I mean. God comes to us speaking whatever language we may require in our lives, whether that language is money or poverty, healing or illness, separation or reconciliation. God works through whatever language we'll hear. That's pretty overwhelming, Bubba, to think that God cares enough about us to do that."

"God cares enough to send the very best - includin' me!"

"Have another yogurt chip."

"Don't mind if I do..."

"But the scary part, Bubba, is the Holy Spirit stuff that Jesus talked about. The part where he said the *world* can't receive the Spirit because it neither knows or sees God coming to it - but *we* can because the spirit dwells *with* us and *in* us."

"What's scary about that?"

"What's scary is that now that the spirit of God has been poured out on us in ways that we can clearly understand - now we have a *choice* as to whether or not we'll USE it."

"That's where y'all are at a disadvantage, son. We angels don't have to worry much about that free choice stuff. The Boss keeps a pretty good eye on us, ya know."

"That's the point, Bubba. Now that the spirit's with us and in us we can choose to accept it or reject it. We decide daily whether we will do the expedient thing or the sacrificial thing, whether we will use our resources to manufacture three nuclear bombs a day or use them to create solar energy and efficient cars, whether to play Macho with other nations or to use our leverage to negotiate meaningful peace, whether to empower the poor and release the captives or to further enslave and turn deaf ears to those in our world family who are powerless. Those choices are scary, Bubba. Having the spirit is scary."

"Oh, I guess it is till ya get the hang of it, son. Takes a while, ya know."

"Well there's no time to start like the present. Pentecost is a good place to make a beginning."

"Sounds good to me, boy. Why not use the Eucharist as a starting point? Ask forgiveness for not using the spirit, for not being open to God's working among you inside and outside the establishment church. Then break bread and drink wine together and go out to do the work God has given you to do - to be the Church (with a capital C) in the world and not just another denomination on Sunday."

"Bubba, did you ever think of taking up preaching?"

"Who do you think wrote Peter's sermon on Pentecost, son? I always did like bein' - you should excuse the expression - a holy ghost writer!"

"Well, thanks for your help, Bubba. Can I give you one for the clouds?" I said, reaching over to pour him another glass.

"No thanks, boy. I got to get a-movin' on. What time is it anyway?"

"It's about 10:30, why?"

"Holy rollin' pentecostals - I'm late again. Sittin' here jawin' with ya I'm gonna be late for my meetin'."

"Not another convention?"

"Nope. Seems some new saint's moved to Austin recently and thrown our whole system out of order. Now we got to meet to decide whose territory is whose again. And just when we had it all mapped out good..."

"Remember, Bubba, the best laid plans of mice and angels..."

"Yea, well, thanks for the hospitality, son - such as it was," he said, getting up and heading for the door.

"Drop bye anytime, Bubba."

"I'll do that, boy. You just keep the Shiner cold," he said. And as he drifted up from the front porch and out of sight he hollered back over his shoulder: "But next time have somethin' better than those crummy yogurt chips!"

I smiled as I walked back into the house hoping I could remember all the words of the holy ghost writer about the tremendously hopeful, tremendously frightening day of Pentecost. And I wondered when I'd see Bubba again.

Genesis 18.1-14

And the Lord appeared to him by the oaks of Mamre, as he sat at the door of his tent in the heat of the day. He lifted up his eyes and looked, and behold, three men stood in front of him. When he saw them, he ran from the tent door to meet them, and bowed himself to the earth, and said, "My lord, if I have found favor in your sight, do not pass by your servant. Let a little water be brought, and wash your feet, and rest yourselves, and after that you may pass on - since you have come to your servant." So they said, "Do as you have said."

And Abraham hastened into the tent to Sarah, and said, "Make ready quickly three measures of fine meal, knead it, and make cakes." And Abraham ran to the herd, and took a calf, tender and good, and gave it to the servant, who hastened to prepare it. Then he took curds, and milk, and the calf which he had prepared, and set it before them; and he stood by them under the tree while they ate.

They said to him, "Where is Sarah your wife?" And he said, "She is in the tent." The Lord said, "I will surely return to you in the spring, and Sarah your wife shall have a son." And Sarah was listening at the tent door behind him. Now Abraham and Sarah were old, advanced in age; it had ceased to be with Sarah after the manner of women. So Sarah laughed to herself, saying, "After I have grown old, and my husband is old, shall I have pleasure?"

The Lord said to Abraham, "Why did Sarah laugh, and say, 'Shall I indeed bear a child, now that I am old?'

Is anything too hard for the Lord? At the appointed time I will return to you, in the spring, and Sarah shall have a son."

Bubba at Deep Eddy

Deep Eddy pool is one of my favorite places in the world. It used to be a kind of resort at a point called "Deep Eddy" on the Colorado just outside of downtown Austin. It is huge and spring fed and filled with young mothers and babies and kids and college students. Its cold water is starkly refreshing on a sultry Austin day, and the sting of that water helps to clear my mind as I'm doing laps or sitting on the side watching people.

As I sat there last Saturday, kicking my legs in the water, looking at no one in particular, wondering what I'd write about the scripture for today, my trance was interrupted by a familiar voice:

"Have a beer, boy, you look like you're about to sweat to death."

"BUBBA!!" I exclaimed. "What're you doing here?" He opened a styrofoam cooler of Shiner Bock. I quickly looked around at the pool attendants and whispered to Bubba: "You can't have any kind of drinks down here in the pool."

"Shore I can!" He pointed a finger in Jedi fashion at each lifeguard and suddenly they seemed not to notice us. "Now that ain't much of a greetin,' boy. You're supposed to be glad to see me!"

He was clad only in orange swim shorts with a longhorn on the back and "Foat Wuth" on the front. The tips of his wings dipped into the water.

"I *am* glad to see you, Bubba...just...uh... uh...surprised is all. Have you lost some weight?"

"Thought you'd never notice, boy. I'm a mere sliver of my old self. Body's the temple of the spirit, ya know, and I got word from the Boss to clean out the temple - if ya know what I mean. Right now I'm in trainin' for the Pearly Gate 10,000." He opened a beer for me.

"I can see you are. But what are you doing *here*"?

"Laps, boy, what else?"

"But your suit's not wet."

"I don't do 'em in the *water*, son. Hate water. It's wet, ya know. Things *breed* in that stuff. Yech! No, I do 'em in the air *over* the water. I was flyin' through my twenty-fourth lap when I heard you thinkin' about the time me and the Boss and another dude..."

"Wait a minute. Are you going to sit there and tell me YOU were at Mamm-ry?"

"That's 'Mahm-re,' boy. Be careful how you say that! You sound like you're from Waco. And of course I was there."

"And of course you're going to tell me about it."

"You bet your inner tube I am! I want to give you the straight scoop."

"I'll take the beer."

"Shore thing," he said, handing it to me from his floating ice chest. "Now, as I was sayin,' me and the Boss and another angel went down to the oaks of Mamre to see Abraham. We was on a messenger mission - sorta like a singin' telegram - and when we got there Abraham got so flustered he didn't wait for us to talk."

"I'll bet he was scared."

"Oh, I don't know. You'd think he'd get used to it after a while. And then, too, the Boss and me made a lot more personal appearances in those days."

"How come?" I asked. "We could sure use you appearing more often today."

"Shoot-fire, boy, back then people could recognize us. If we did that today they'd lock y'all up in a Houston minute. We still appear, and a lot more regular than you'd guess. We just put a bit more shade on it now."

"So go on."

"Oh, yeah. So Abraham runs off before we can get a word in edgewise, kills a calf, has Sarah bake some cakes, and washes our feet. He really showed us some down home Southern Israel hospitality."

"You would remember the food."

"I mean...that boy could flat cook some barbecue!!"

"Now you're making *me* hungry."

He reached behind his back to the floating cooler. "Here, have a sandwich."

"Where'd you get these, Bubba?"

"I stopped at - where else - Thundercloud Subs, on the way over."

"Well, thanks. What happened after the feast?"

"As I recall it was *me* who asked where Sarah was."

"Of course..."

"We wanted her to hear the message, ya see."

"And Abraham told you she was in the tent?"

"Yep. Then the Boss told him about their son to be born in the spring."

"And Sarah laughed."

Bubba glared at me. "Who's tellin' this story, boy, you or me?"

"You are."

"That's right."

"So what happened?"

"Sarah laughed."

"Right. But that makes *sense* to me, Bubba. I don't know if she was laughing at the ridiculousness of the news or at the hysteria of the thought. How'd *you* like to be 93 and have a kid in diapers?"

"Why I was a lot older than that when....but that's another story. Actually I wasn't real surprised, boy. People been laughin' at the Boss since time began."

"They're *still* laughing at him, Bubba. Mention

gun control and people laugh. Talk about reallocating resources to heal our sick and feed our hungry poor, and people snicker. Work for protection and pre- servation of the environment and hear the chuckles. Say out loud that because we *can* do something technologically doesn't mean we *should* ethically, and get hooted down. Live a just life in an unjust world and be ridiculed. Face it, Bubba, God is just plain ridiculous from our society's point of view."

"Careful Who you're callin' ridiculous, boy! Don't you know lightnin' likes to strike swimmin' pools?"

"Well, it's *true*. And God's not only ridiculous, he's also *inappropriate*. God's always coming into people's lives at the wrong places, breaking in unin- vited at the wrong time, saying inappropriate things that don't fit the way we want to see and do things. In fact, God's downright *disruptive*, Bubba. Imagine having a 13 year old adolescent running around the house when you're 106. God is always doing the equivalent of that to us, shaking our foundations, confronting us with our worship of the status quo, presenting us with absurdities to show us how silly and scared we are and how open and loving we could be if we'd only trust Him and let ourselves be."

"I guess the Boss just has a different sense of tim- ing than you do, boy. His schedule runs on Central Sacred Time - and that just doesn't measure things in human terms entirely. In fact, the Boss is sort of oblivious to time in general - it all looks like *right now* to him. Makes workin' for him real interestin' sometimes."

"I can understand that. It probably seemed to him like *just* the right time for Sarah to have that baby. I think where I get in trouble sometimes is - just like Abraham and Sarah - judging God by *my* standards, like time for instance."

"Not just time, boy. Other things too - things like power, justice, love, prayer, barbecue. The Boss sees those things a lot different than ya'll do."

I was about to respond to his comment on the barbecue when Bubba let out a jolting yell.

"AAAARRRRGGGGHHHH!!! You got *sharks* in this pool, boy? What is that thing hangin' on my leg?"

"That's a kid, Bubba. I thought nobody could see you?"

"Cain't see me, but if they bump into me it usually scares 'em some. That Jedi stuff doesn't work too well with rug rats anyway. Get that little ankle nipper off'n my leg before I get any wetter than I am."

I peeled the kid off his shin as Bubba started to leave.

"Got to do some more laps, son. Guard that beer good for me. I may drop in for it sometime."

"Hey," I said as he took his position above the lap lanes and began doing the back stroke in mid air, "...don't leave yet. I need some more stuff for Sunday."

"Just tell 'em to be mighty careful how they respond to the Boss, boy, because that's how they'll be labeled for the rest of their lives."

"Come back here!" I protested. "What do you mean by that?"

"You remember the name of that kid that Abraham and Sarah had?" he said, switching to the side stroke.

"Sure. It was 'Isaac.'"

"There you go again, son, talkin' like you're from East Texas. The boy's name was 'YIZZAC' — and it means 'HE LAUGHS.'"

"If that's the case, Bubba, there are a lot of us in church with names like 'HE DOUBTS,' 'SHE WONDERS,' 'HE CRIES,' 'SHE WANTS,' 'HE LIES,' 'SHE HATES,' 'HE CHEATS,' 'SHE USES,' 'HE LUSTS.'"

"Of course there are, son. So pay close attention to how y'all react to God's bad timing in your life. Your reaction could label who you are forever."

"Well, I'll be gosh-darned."

"You certainly will be, boy."

"What?"

"I forgot to tell you, son..." Bubba said as he became less and less visible, "...When I vanish everybody can see you *and* that case of Shiner floatin' in the pool beside you."

"Oh no," I cried.

"Bye, son," he said, now completely disappeared. "Ya'll have fun."

"BUBBAAAA!!" I yelled to no avail. Astonished swimmers gawked as three lifeguards blew their whistles and began converging on me. "You ought to change *your* name to 'Isaac!'"

"Not a bad idea," came the smiling voice from nowhere. "Not a bad idea at all."

Luke: 10.38-42

As Jesus and his disciples went on their way, Jesus entered a village; and a woman named Martha received him into her house. And she had a sister called Mary, who sat at the Lord's feet and listened to his teaching. But Martha was distracted with much serving; and she went to him and said, "Lord, do you not care that my sister has left me to serve alone? Tell her then to help me." But the Lord answered her, "Martha, Martha, you are anxious and troubled about many things; one thing is needful. Mary has chosen the good portion, which shall not be taken away from her."

Peaches and Beer

I did nothing to deserve it. I didn't water it. I didn't fertilize it. I didn't spray it for bugs. All I did about nine years ago was to plant the peach tree and ignore it. In fairness, I must add that it ignored me also, as it produced absolutely no peaches for lo these many years. So, for the last two years, I did more than ignore it - I forgot about it.

Then about a week ago, I opened the gate to run the lawn mower over the wall to wall fire ant mounds that I jokingly call my back yard - and there they were. Peaches! And not just two or three peaches, but a whole red and yellow tree full.

Gorgeous fuzzy spheres clung lazily to their leafy hats. Limbs bent to the ground with the heaviness of the juicy ripe fruit. In some miraculous way, it was as though I had happened upon them at the very instant they ripened. Although there were birds lined up on the back fence, they and their insect cronies had not yet descended and so the peaches were ready for picking.

In gratefulness for this abundance, I vowed to share some with my neighbors and friends at work and got some buckets to begin my pleasant task. I had filled one bucket and was busily filling a second when a familiar voice startled me.

"Why, boy, that's right nice of you to offer me some of this here good fruit of your labors."

"BUBBA!!!" I exclaimed, kicking over one pail and dropping the other.

"Don't kick the bucket, boy!" Bubba laughed so hard his belly jiggled.

"Very funny, Ozone Breath," I muttered.

"What was that?" Bubba said, recovering himself.

"I said, do you *HAVE* to sneak up on people all the time?"

"Sneak up? Sneak UP? Boy, I was makin' more noise with my wings than a passle of doggies, tryin' to get yore attention - and there you are, busy at work ig-norin' me as usual...Why it reminds me of the story of Mary and Martha..."

"Clever...very clever..." I said, picking up the buckets and continuing to work on the tree. "How did *you* know I had to talk about that next Sunday?"

"How did I know? It's my *bidness* to know, boy! And I also know that you don't understand what went on there, so I thought I'd drop by to fill you in on the straight scoop, as it were."

"Do I want to hear this?"

"Probably not, but that never stopped me before..."

"Well, can you talk and pick peaches at the same time? I could use some help with this and..."

"Boy, that's yore problem..."

"What's my problem?"

"Always havin' to be busy all the time. Don't you know nothin' about re-laxin'?"

"If I 're-lax,' as you put it, those birds are gonna eat all these great peaches and you won't get any either."

Bubba looked at the birds on the fence and back at the peaches.

"Okay, son. But just for a minute or two. I cain't stand out here in the sun very long. It gives me cloud ache."

"Cloud ache?"

"Like a head ache but higher up."

We started picking the wonderful fruit, and Bubba just kept on talking.

"Yeah. That Mary and Martha were quite a pair."

"You *knew* them?"

"Does a bear sneeze in the woods? Of course I knew them, boy. Had dinner at their house lots of times. That Martha could cook up some cornbread and beans that would make your mouth do flips."

"And the next thing you're going to tell me is that you were *there* when..."

"Well, as a matter of fact I *was*, son."

"Okay - so grab those peaches off the top branch up there and tell me what happened."

"I thought you'd never ask." He flapped his wings and ascended to the top of the small tree, grabbed some peaches and floated back to the ground.

"Seems that Mary and Martha were in their house and Martha heard Jesus was coming. She ran down the street and invited him in for a spell. But no sooner had he hit the door, than Martha ran off to the kitchen and Mary plopped herself right down in front of Jesus, lookin' at him sorta awe-struck like and just listenin' to anything he said for all she was worth."

"So what's wrong with that? I mean, *somebody* had to keep him company while Martha was fixing dinner, didn't they? That would have been rude to just leave him sitting there, pouring his own Sherry and slicing his own cheese and crackers."

Bubba glared at me.

"I be-lieve there was a little somethin' more to it than that, son."

"Like what...oh, get the peach over on the end of that branch will you?"

"You're doin' it again, boy."

"Doing WHAT? I'm picking peaches and you're telling me what to say Sunday. What's wrong with that?"

"You're doin' just what Martha was doin' back then! Here I am tryin' to talk to you like a civilized angel and are you payin' attention? No! You're interested in feedin' your jowls and keepin' those poor little birdies from havin' a free lunch."

"Now, wait a minute. Martha was doing the right thing. She was concerned about being a good hostess, fixing something they all would like, working hard in the kitchen, slaving over a hot stove - she wasn't exactly going to whip out a Swanson's and nuke it for them."

"Course she wasn't, son! But what did she invite him in for in the first place - dinner?"

"I give up - why DID she invite him in?"

"Why does *anyone* invite Jesus into their house or their life, son?"

"I don't know - lots of reasons - as many reasons as there are people in church I guess. Some want to know him better. Some are scared. Some think it's the right thing to do. Some are just grateful for their lives and want to share it with him. And some want some miraculous cure for something. Maybe she wanted to know how to get the lumps out of her gravy."

A ripe peach suddenly exploded against my chest.

"Careful, boy. Next time I won't *miss*..."

"Well how am *I* supposed to know what she wanted? YOU'RE the angel - *you* tell me!"

"The point *isn't* what she *wanted*, boy. I mean, will you *ever* get the hang of this Bible stuff?" He vanished behind a branch. "The *point* is that she invited him in and then disappeared."

"But she was disappearing to SERVE him, Bubba. I thought that's what we're *supposed* to do with our lives - SERVE God in one way or another."

"Well, you do have *that* right, son. Of *course* you're supposed to serve The Boss - uh, God - but you got to get yore priorities in order."

"Meaning Mary did and Martha didn't?"

"Not exactly," Bubba said from up in the air over the tree. "Look at what happened - tell me about it as you recall it."

"Okay - Martha disappeared. Then the story says she 'was distracted with much serving,' and went to complain to Jesus and have him make Mary help."

"That's exactly right, son. And that's exactly what happens to y'all."

"What?" I hollered up into the tree. I knew he was up there somewhere.

His voice replied: "Y'all invite Jesus into your lives and then vamoose on him. Sometimes you get all involved in some service project and forget why you started on it in the first place. You know - like bein' on a committee or somethin' and gettin' a burr under yore saddle about other members as if they don't know from nothin' about nothin.' Or you do it at work, or at home with yore family. Or, sometimes, y'all invite Jesus in and vamoose by going on about your lives and ignoring him completely..."

"But Martha wasn't ignoring him...she was..."

"Boy..!" Bubba hollered through the branches,

"...if Jesus was sittin' in *yore* livin' room, would *you* be out here pickin' peaches for him?"

"Oh,...." I reconsidered. "I guess you're right."

"Course I'm right, boy! You keep forgettin' who the angel is around here."

I heard his wings flutter to the ground as he continued. "So like I was sayin'...Martha gets distracted - like we all do - with much serving, or whatever, and gets so stressed out she comes back to drag *Mary* off *with* her and leave poor old Jesus sittin' there with his disciples hangin' around wonderin' what in the world they got invited in for."

"But Jesus seems to recognize her problem, Bubba. He says her name *twice*, as if to calm her down, or get her attention."

"Right, boy. And what does he say?"

"He says she's troubled about too many things - as if her problem is she's trying do too much at once. That's another real problem we have today. Everybody's trying to do everything at once. Stress is one of the major contributors to all kinds of diseases. Getting the dog fed and defleaed, the kids off to school clothed, ourselves to work, the kids to extracurricular activities and social events, ourselves to meetings, family obligations, bills, shopping - the list is endless."

"That's exactly the point, boy. That list, just like Martha's, *is* endless. And what does Jesus say about it?"

"He says she's troubled about many things, when only ONE is needful." I looked down at my over-weight angel friend. "And which one is that, Bubba?"

"*Be-er!*"

"'BEER'???"

"Oh, gosh, boy! Yes. I mean no. I mean I'm sorry. I was sittin' here listenin' to you jabber on about Martha and the one needful thing, and I got thinkin' about how a nice cold beer would go pretty good with these here peaches."

"Beer and peaches? You've been *eating* the peaches?"

"Only ten or twelve of 'em, boy. Why you countin'? You savin' 'em for somethin'? You got an-other angel comin' in to write yore story for ya later on tonight?"

"Okay, okay. I'm sorry. Eat however many you want...but peaches and beer?"

"You got *yore* tastes, boy. I got *mine.*"

I ran in to the kitchen and got us each a cold Shiner.

"Here you go. Now tell me about this one 'need-ful' thing."

"I already told ya, son."

"What?"

"I already told ya what the one needful thing was."

"No you didn't! You said you wanted a beer!"

"No I didn't! You asked what it was and I said 'BE-ER.' *That's* the most important thing in your life.

Be a *be*-er, and not just a *do*-er."

"Are you telling me that *being* is more important than *doing*?"

"Absolutely. Now don't get me wrong. It's important to do more than lie around at Jesus' feet and go to la-la land thinkin' he's going to solve all yore problems. He's not! He didn't even solve Martha's when she wanted him to get Mary off her doofus and help out. But he helped her see an even more important underlyin' problem, boy."

"Let me see if I've got this," I said. "The problem, Bubba, was that she got so involved in her *doing* that she forgot how to BE with people - to listen to them, to spend time with them, to relax and enjoy them and herself with them. I think we do that alot, Bubba; give people monetary gifts rather than our quality time and attention. And Americans think they have to be *busy* all the time with video games or movies, or going somewhere, or accomplishing something, or extra hard at work as though the personal value of our lives depended on it. That's why so many people die soon after they retire. They figure, since they aren't *doing* anything, they aren't *worth* anything. And being - with one another, alone and with God - it's the *being* that's the most important."

"Exactly right, boy. It's just like you and these here peaches. Tryin' to talk to me and pick peaches

like they was gonna vanish if you didn't get it all
done."

"Okay, okay. But what about this 'good portion'
stuff? That part's really got me puzzled."

"I can see by the look in your bloodshot eye that
you think it has to do with the size of the plate, boy!"

"Bubba!"

"Just joshin.' But it sorta does."

"What?"

"I mean the 'good portion' means that what *Mary*
chose *can* as Jesus told Martha, 'never be taken from
her.'"

I looked at him.

"Let me spell it out for ya, boy." He took a bucket
of peaches and put them in front of me. "Now see
these here peaches?"

"Yes."

"Now if you eat all of these peaches, what have
you got?"

"A bad stomach ache?"

Another ripe peach splattered in my lap.

"Pay attention, son!" He tried again. "If you eat
all of these here peaches, what do you have left in
the bucket?" He cast me a threatening glance and
picked up a peach.

"Pits! You've got the *pits* left!"

"Good. Not great, but good." He tossed the peach
in the air and caught it as he talked. "Now. What do

you have after I leave here today?"

I was about to make a smart remark but did not want to get beaned - or peached - again, so I said: "A memory?"

"A what?"

"A pleasant memory?"

"A what?"

"A very pleasant memory with a story written!" I cringed. "Just don't hit me with that thing!"

"I cain't help it sometimes, boy. Yore such a good target." He put the peach down. "But you are catchin' on. That's right. A memory. An experience of a person, or, in my case, a angel. And now which one is lasting? The peach pits or the memory of time with me?"

"I'll bet I'm supposed to say the memory of the time with you?"

"You're supposed to, 'cause it's *true*. And that's just what Jesus meant!"

"Yeah! I get it, Bubba. They can take food away. They can take away the ability to *do* things - like when someone is disabled by accident or disease - but nobody can take away the *memories* of time together, whether listening to the Word of God, being fed by it, or listening to one another, spending time with ones we love, relaxing, giving up some of the stress we demand of ourselves to spend good quality time with one another and with God, instead of talking or praying on the run all the time."

"I do believe you got it, boy," Bubba said, standing up to stretch. "Well, I had about all the fun I can stand with you for now. You better get back to your peach pickin' before them birdies get a peach ahead of you."

"Okay, okay. I can take a hint. I'll slow down. And I *did* enjoy talking and listening to you, much as I hate to admit it."

"Good. Now you go and tell them all that at church next week."

I nodded as he ascended up above the house. "Wait a minute, Bubba! Why don't you take some peaches with you?"

"I knew you'd want me to, so I already did, boy! Thanks." I looked up to see him carrying a huge white bag overflowing with the red and yellow fruit.

"Oh, great, Bubba! Those are all the ones it took me so long to pick."

"Right! You're gettin' more generous every day, son."

I hollered after him. "Hey, Bubba! I just figured out the moral to that story about being and doing!"

"What's that, boy!"

"'Peaches may come and peaches may go, but life with Bubba is always the pits!'"

"That's clever, boy! That's *real* clever!" he said as he vanished out of sight.

I chuckled to myself, having gotten the last laugh for a change. A whizzing noise caused me to look up

- just in time to see a juicy ripe object aiming for my head.

The waiting birds fled from the fence at the sound of the giant *SPLAT*.

Luke 2.1-7

In those days a decree went out from Caesar Augustus that all the world should be enrolled. This was the first enrollment, when Quirinius was governor or Syria. And all went to be enrolled, each to his own city. And Joseph also went up from Galilee, from the city of Nazareth, to Judea, to the city of David, which is called Bethlehem, because he was of the house and lineage of David, to be enrolled with Mary, his betrothed, who was with child.

And while they were there, the time came for her to be delivered. And she gave birth to her first-born son and wrapped him in swaddling cloths, and laid him in a manger, because there was no place for them in the inn.

Bubba and Harold the Innkeeper

There I was, sitting at the word processor, wondering what to tell the congregation about Christmas this year. In past years I'd told them about the Donkey Named Glory, the Star Named Tink, the Shepherds And Bubba, and The Fourth Wise Man. What was left to tell? As I sat, scratching my head and frowning, I suddenly heard a deep voice in the chair behind me.

"Tell him about the Innkeeper named Harold!"

I nearly fell out of my seat as I whirled around to see that huge angel in my favorite leather reclining chair, with a Shiner Bock in one hand and a bowl of popcorn in the other. His large wings were draped over the back of the chair.

"BUBBA!" I exclaimed. "What are *you* doing here?"

"A fine greetin' boy! A fine greetin.' Why, I even had to make my own popcorn and get my own drink. And me on a mission of mercy, too."

"Mission of mercy?"

"Yep. I was makin' my rounds and saw you down here fumblin' around, tryin' to spin a story for that church crowd...so I knew I'd better drop in and tell you what really happened, so they wouldn't be so confused."

I resisted the temptation to dump the bowl of popcorn on his head. The last time I did something like that he sat on me 'till he finished his story. Besides, I'd never heard this one before.

"And I suppose you know what really happened because you were there?"

"Does a dog have fleas, boy? Of **course** I was there!" Bubba lowered his normally booming voice. "But I was in-cog-nito. I was dis-guised!"

I pointed to his large belly. "As what - an overfed water buffalo?"

"Very funny, boy. Very funny," he said, ignoring me to get on with his story. "I was disguised, for your information, as a weary traveler lookin' for a room. That's how I know about Harold the Innkeeper."

"You mean you got to that inn before Joseph and Mary?"

"That's right, boy. Old Harold refused me a room before he refused them one. That's how I know there was no room at the inn, and what Harold's problem was."

I propped my feet up and leaned back in my chair. "Okay," I said. "You've got my attention. Tell me the story."

"Thought you'd never ask, son," Bubba said, taking a drink and swallowing a handful of popcorn. "It was like this...Every now and then we angels dress up like you humans and check things out for the Boss, like how kind or helpful or generous you are."

"I guess I blew it on the popcorn, huh?"

"Don't worry. I'll give you another chance later." He munched down more of the fluffy stuff. "Anyway, I was checkin' out some of the people there in Bethlehem, when I wandered into the inn run by Harold."

"Last name?"

"Daye. And he named it after his wife whose name was, uh...Holly."

"The Holly Daye Inn?" I groaned.

"Catchy, huh? But try not to interrupt me, boy...where was I?"

"You were checking into the Holly Daye Inn."

"Yeah. And I went up to the counter and there was Harold the Innkeeper looking upset and dejected. It seems that one of his twin boys - John - had wandered off somewhere and hadn't been seen for days. Holly was very upset, and Harold was trying his best to keep the inn running at full tilt and look for the boy, too.

"But Harold was frazzled. Worn to the bone. Stressed to the max. Circuits fried. So he wasn't in too cordial a mood when I rang the bell on the desk. I noticed that a couple of mail slots behind the desk had keys in them and so I was surprised when he told me there were no rooms available. I guess he looked me over when I came in and decided that, since I wasn't wearing the best of clothes, he could get a higher price for those rooms from one of the many wealthy travelers passin' though Bethlehem that weekend. When he told me those rooms belonged to his family and he couldn't rent them, the little boy (about nine years old) standing behind him peeped his head out and tugged on his father's shirt. He had a mop of black hair that nearly covered his huge brown eyes."

"Daddy?" he said.

"Don't bother me now, Amahl. I'm working."

"But Daddy...those rooms...?"

Harold the Innkeeper glared at his son. "They are full, Amahl. Now go help your mother in the kitchen, and keep an eye out for your brother."

"Amahl left and Harold apologized for the boy. He explained they had all been on edge since John disappeared two days before - especially since a Spanish circus had passed through town at the very same time. In fact, John had last been seen playing with one of the circus kids on the edge of town.

"Anyway, Harold said there was no room in the inn. Either he wasn't a very good liar, or he remembered that you should always treat strangers well because they might be angels in disguise, because he did soften a little and recommended a flophouse down in the other end of town."

"What happened then? Did Joseph and Mary show up?"

"Don't rush me, boy. I'm runnin' out of popcorn."

I quickly made another batch and returned with enough to last us both long into the night.

"Thanks, son. Now, as I was sayin'...uh...what was I sayin'?"

"You were leaving the Holly Daye Inn because there was supposedly no room, but you didn't tell me where you went."

"Oh, yeah, sure, I remember now...I was leavin' the inn. But you know, I got to worryin' about poor old Harold, tryin' to make ends meet and distracted about poor little John and all...and then there was that other cute little fella...."

"I thought you didn't like kids...?"

"I don't! Cain't stand the little curtain climbers! But this kid was tuggin' on his Daddy and lookin' so pitiful...Well, I didn't have much time to think about it as it turned out."

"John came back?"

"Will you *hush* and let me tell this? Stuff some of that popcorn in yore face or somethin'."

I sighed and leaned back in the chair.

"Now here's what happened. And lissen up good, 'cause you'll have to tell it to the church when I'm through."

I nodded.

"Just as I was leavin' the place I heard the 'clomp, clomp' of hooves on the cobblestone street leadin' up to the inn. I hung back in a doorway and watched a very tired Joseph leading the poor old donkey with an agonizing Mary on its back. They saw me standin' there and asked if I could help. I said (and I was later quoted in a famous Southern movie): 'I don't know nothin' about birthin' babies.' But it turned out they just wanted directions to the nearest inn and I pointed them to Harold and Holly's place - knowing what would happen."

"Why did you do that? Why didn't you just send them someplace else?"

Bubba sat forward in the chair and looked at me, wide-eyed. "You don't mess with *symbols* boy!"

"Symbols? What's so symbolic about being refused at the Holly Daye Inn?"

"Boy, where *did* you go to seminary?" Bubba asked, wolfing down another handful of popcorn and washing it down with the rest of the Shiner. "The *symbolism* is that, for the rest of Jesus' life - beginning with his even trying to find a place to BE BORN - there would be 'no room in the inn' of people's lives for him. Either they're too busy, or too upset, or too tied down by obligations, or too scared, or too distracted by others, or too worried about takin' a chance and bein' associated with him (he's not always well-dressed, you know), or like Harold, hoping to fill their lives with something better than Jesus, or maybe even thinking Jesus wouldn't stay there with them if they DID invite him in. For whatever reason — from the very beginning until right up to now — there's been no room in the inn of people's lives for Jesus." Bubba looked satisfied with his explanation and leaned back in his chair. "...and *that's* the symbol, boy."

I looked skeptically at him. "And you expect the congregation to understand...?"

"They're smart folks. You just tell them the world's been trying to keep Jesus out from the time Jesus was born. Everybody knows how it feels not to be wanted in a game or by friends. All people do." Bubba nodded his head. "Trust me."

"You bet...so you directed them to the inn?"

"Yes. And Harold the Innkeeper did it again. He told them there was no room. But — and I know this because I used my special angel-hearing to listen to their conversation — Amahl tugged on his Daddy's shirt again and pointed to the pregnant Mary with a look of sadness in his eyes.

"'Daddy,' he said, '...How about the barn out back? I'll go clean out a spot for them.' So Harold took compassion on them and said they could stay in the barn, and Amahl went out and helped them get settled as best they could. He scattered the pigs and chickens and cows into other stalls and got the warmest one ready for the tired man and the slowly moving woman. He even put down some fresh straw for them to lie upon."

"I think I know the rest of the story, Bubba," I said confidently.

"No you don't."

"Yes I do."

"No you don't!"

"Yes I do!"

"Your problem, boy, is that you keep forgettin' who the angel is around here," Bubba said, staring at me. "And if you know the rest of the story - tell me how John got back?"

"John who?"

"How can you know the rest of the story if you cain't even keep the characters straight?" he glared at me. "John the twin brother!"

I thought a second, tapped my foot and raised my eyebrows. Then I said: "So continue."

"Thank you very much," Bubba said sarcastically. "Now, before I was thrown off track, I think that Joseph and Mary had just gotten into the barn."

I added, "And Amahl had cleaned a stall for them where a couple of cows had been lying so the straw was still nice and warm."

"How did you know that?" Bubba asked.

"Elementary, my dear Bubba," I grinned. "Amahl's a nice kid. He'd do something like that."

"Well, it just so happens that he did," Bubba said reluctantly. "And that's when I knew it was time for me to go find his brother."

"Why?"

"Well, I figured that maybe, with a little help, that family could come around. And, after all, Harold the Innkeeper did let Mary and Joseph have a place to go to have the baby," Bubba smiled. "Matter of fact, no sooner did Mary lie down on the hay than that baby started to be born."

"How did you know where to look for John?"

"Simple, boy," Bubba grinned. "Harold said he was last seen with the circus kids. So I unfolded my wings from under the cape I wore and took off in the night sky to find their encampment. It was easy to see because there was such great starlight coming from one special star shining down over Bethlehem that night. I found the camp about 20 miles away and softly landed behind one of the circus tents. I went invisible and slowly walked through the camp, looking at the children. It wasn't until I came to the very last tent that I saw him. The other kids were calling him by the name they used in Spanish - 'Juan' instead of 'John.'

"Since they were just going to sleep I waited a few minutes until all the lanterns were out and their breathing stilled. Then I scooped up Juan and took off into the sky once again. He woke up once but thought he was just dreaming and slumped back into the blanket in my arms.

"Just as I landed by the stable door, the cry of a little baby broke the silence and the darkness of the night. I don't know how to explain this to you, boy, except to say that it was like a light that came into the world all of a sudden-like, a light that made everything look different; sorta like a kid hidin' under the covers of his bed and turnin' on a flashlight - except that this light was permanent, and no matter how dark it got, this light would always be there, not lettin' anybody ever again be in total darkness."

"And John woke up?"

"Yeah, he did. He woke up and went into the barn where his brother Amahl was sitting cross-legged watching the baby Jesus and Mary and Joseph all bundled up together. The two brothers hugged and looked at the baby and John told his brother how he had run away to join the circus, but it wasn't all it was cracked up to be and he was glad to be home — though he wasn't exactly sure how that had happened.

"Then they both went and woke their parents and pulled them, crying and laughing, back into the barn to see the newborn baby Jesus. Their parents fell to their knees and prayed a prayer of thanks for the safe return of their son. And, because I'm an angel, I knew that the Boss was glad that they had provided a safe place for His son to be born, too."

As Bubba sat back looking satisfied with himself, I quickly scribbled a few more notes on my pad so I could write this all down for the church. Then I looked up to ask Bubba another question that had occurred to me.

But he was gone, the popcorn bowl was empty and the Shiner bottle was lying on its side. Bubba had finished what he had come to do and was off to take care of his other chores. He did leave a note, though. It said, "Whatever you do, boy, don't call this story "Christmas at the Holly Daye Inn." So I didn't. I called it "Harold The Innkeeper."

Later that night I got to wondering how Bubba knew that the boy in the tent was really John with the light so dim and Bubba's eyes not being what they used to be a few hundred years ago. The next morning I found a note on my desk that read: "Simple, boy. When you've seen Juan - you've seen Amahl!"

Micah 6.1-8

Hear what the Lord says:
Arise, plead your case before the mountains
and let the hills hear your voice.
Hear, you mountains, the controversy of the Lord,
and you enduring foundations of the earth;
for the Lord has a controversy with his people,
and he will contend with Israel.
"O my people, what have I done to you?
In what have I wearied you?
Answer me!
For I brought you up from the land of Egypt,
and redeemed you from the house of bondage;
and I sent before you Moses, Aaron, and Miriam.
O my people, remember what Balak king of Moab
     devised
and what Balaam the son of Beor answered him,
and what happened from Shittim to Gilgal,
that you may know the saving acts of the Lord.
With what shall I come before the Lord,
and bow myself before God on high?
Shall I come before him with burnt offerings,
with a calf a year old?
Will the Lord be pleased with thousands of rams,
with ten thousands of rivers of oil?
Shall I give my first-born for my transgression,
     the fruit of my body for the sin of my soul?"
     He has showed you, O man, what is good;
     and what does the Lord require of you
     but to do justice, and to love kindness,
     and to walk humbly with your God?

I Corinthians 1.26-31

``For consider your call, brethren; not many of you were wise according to worldly standards, not many were powerful, not many were of noble birth; but God chose what is foolish in the world to shame the wise, God chose what is weak in the world to shame the strong, God chose what is low and despised in the world, even things that are not, to bring to nothing things that are, so that no human being might boast in the presence of God. He is the source of your life in Christ Jesus, whom God made our wisdom, our righteousness and sanctification and redemption; therefore, as it is written, "Let him who boasts, boast of the Lord."

Bubba at Dime Box

T here are two things that you need to know to understand this story. The first is that I am an addict. My desire takes me to small Texas towns like Dime Box and Oatmeal and Luling and Schwertner. It leads me to collect strange articles of clothing and wear them in public with a weird sense of pride. It pushes my body to do things it ought not to have done, and sometimes appears to be hastening the ultimate release of my soul into a heaven that I can only hope is replete with the means to support this insatiable addiction - to *running*.

I know it is hard on my knees. I know my heart rate exceeds the maximum necessary or even desirable for extended periods of time. I know that the only two good reasons for running are the t-shirts and the beer, and I could have those with much less pain and sweat - but still I run.

Secondly, as you must know by now, I have acquired an angel named Bubba who shows up from time to time to help me write stories, give advice, and tell me how it really was back then, is now and shall be forever. He appears and disappears at the worst possible times, never when I want him, leaving me to explain what nobody else can see. He makes me feel like Cosmo Topper. And it is with that background that the following story unfolds.

I had just arrived in Dime Box, Texas and was looking forward to the Dime Box Mini-Marathon. It was only a 10K run and my knees felt up to doing it at a relaxed pace. I found my way to the starting line and stretched as best I could in the time I had left. I was by myself and kept watching for familiar faces of other runners in the crowd. Not seeing any, I dropped back the proper distance from the line to give the serious contenders their space, and waited for the shotgun blast to begin the race.

The gun went off and a cheer went up from the crowd. I smiled at the anonymous enthusiasm and started off at my usual steady pace, remembering I had 6.2 miles to cover and I'd best not wear myself out on the first two. I was jogging along at a nice speed for me, enjoying the fresh air and the cows and the hay and the morning mist in the air when I noticed a rather heavy breathing runner approaching from behind.

At first I didn't pay much attention to it. Every race has folks who think 6 miles is a snap and are so out of shape they collapse or drop out after a half mile or so. But the more I listened, the more something stirred in my brain. That puffing and panting sounded — familiar.

"No. It couldn't be," I said to myself. "He wouldn't come out in the middle of nowhere. Furthermore he wouldn't go to the inconvenience of actually exerting himself and sweating just to catch up with me."

Suddenly a huge mountain of a figure jogged up beside me, eclipsing the morning sun from my sight.

"Course I would, son! Besides, this here runnin' business fits right into my exercise plan."

"Bubba!!" I exclaimed, nearly tripping as I jumped to avoid stepping in the presents left by cows who had recently preceded us down that same country road. "What are *you* doing here?"

"I can tell you're glad to see me as always, boy. You know, just once I wish you'd say something like 'Whoopee-do you're a sight for sore eyes,' or 'Gee I'm glad to see you' or 'Why don't we stop this stupid running and sit down and talk like civilized people?'"

I looked at him out of the corner of my eye. If I ignored him he'd talk me to death till I stopped. Maybe if I kept arguing with him he'd keep running. "No, Bubba. I am not going to stop and listen to you."

"Sure you are, son. So why not just give up now and save us both a lot of hassle."

I looked over at him and frowned.

"Besides," he said, "I know you're havin' trouble with that story of yours for them folks up at the church..."

"How did you know...?"

"How do I know *anything* boy! I'm an *angel*, and don't you forget it."

I decided to keep talking and running at the same time. "Well," I said, cleverly picking up my pace a bit, "I do have some questions about those texts."

"Fire away, boy. Fire away."

I was about to speak when I suddenly lost my footing and went sprawling out on the pavement. Bubba was over me in a minute, helping me up.

"What happened, son?"

"I think you tripped me, you big..."

"Watch it now, boy. Watch who you're accusin'." He pointed behind me. "Look back there at that big ol' rock in the road. That's what you tripped over."

I eyed him suspiciously. I was certain that rock had not been there before. "Are you sure...?"

"Course I am, son. Now why don't you just come over here off the road and let's us sit down under this big tree and talk a spell."

He helped me up and steadied me as we walked off the road and sat down. Other runners went by as though we were invisible, and I realized Bubba had "fixed it" so we *were*.

"Wait right here, son," he said, walking around the tree and pulling out a large cooler. "Here..." He handed me a brown, icy cold bottle of Shiner Bock. "This'll help you heal up better."

"Bubba! You DID trip me! You knew right where you stashed that cooler and..."

"Pure coincidence, boy. Pure coincidence. But are you gonna waste our time moanin' about that or do you want somethin' to say on Sunday?"

I knew I was beaten, at least for now. "Okay. Go ahead. Speak to me," I said, and sullenly sipped on the Shiner.

"What do you want to know?" the huge figure asked.

"I want to know about justice."

"'Justice?'"

"Yeah. 'Justice.'"

"What about it?"

"Well, I don't get it, Bubba. I mean, Micah says to *do justice*."

"Yeah. I like that passage. I liked it when he wrote it. It's all you need to know about how to live. It's right up there with the two things Jesus said to do."

"But what *is* it? I mean, what *is* justice? Sometimes, like in the Psalm it seems like it's vindication, and if you wait long enough the bad guys will get theirs. Is justice a matter of *time*?"

"Nope. Time's got nothing to do with it. Unless of course yore talkin' about eternity. The Boss don't know too much about time - past, present and future and like that. It's all sort of the same moment to

Him. That's why the Boss don't wear a watch." Bubba pointed to my wrist. If He did it would just say 'NOW'."

"Well is justice like what they used to say at the penitentiary where I worked?"

"What was that?"

"'What goes around comes around.' Like karma or yin yang or if you do unto others it'll come right back to you?"

"Naw, that ain't it either." Bubba took a long sip of Shiner and looked off into the distance. "Let's see, how do I explain this to the boy? Justice, justice...." Suddenly his eyes brightened up and he looked back at me. "I got it!" He glanced up to the clouds. "Thanks, Boss."

"You got what? Cramps?" I looked down the road and watched all the runners getting ahead of us. "Do you know how far behind I'm gonna be on account of you?"

"Forget the race, son. I'll take care of that later. You wanted to know about justice? I got it!" Bubba took a deep breath and smiled. "Justice is.. Justice is...*God's sense of humor*."

I stared at him blankly. "'Justice is God's sense of humor?' That's *it*? You're telling me that I am supposed to stand up in the pulpit on Sunday and tell them an overweight angel drinking Shiner beer told me 'Justice is God's sense of humor?'"

"Yep," he smiled proudly. "But you can leave out

the overweight part."

"*God* has a sense of humor?"

"Course he does, son. He made *you* didn't he?"

"Bubba!"

"And he made the first Apostles, didn't he? I mean, you never saw a sorrier bunch of rag tag ne'er-do-wells in all your days. Why, I could tell you stuff about them that would make your..."

"Bubba! What're you talking about?"

"And them folks in that church Sunday, also."

"Bubba, I can't tell them that. I mean..."

"Course you can, and you'd better, too, boy. Remember what Paul said."

"Which thing?"

"'Woe to me if I do *not* preach the Gospel.'"

"Meaning?"

"Meaning, *preach* it, boy. Tell it like it is. The Boss's got a heck of a sense of humor. He made you, me, the apostles, those folks in the church, *all* of us, whether we've got drug problems, or marriage problems, or single problems, or drinkin' problems, or kid problems, or out of work problems, or oil problems, or depression problems. No matter what it is, the Boss keeps on loving us towards justice."

"But I thought justice had something to do with *equality*."

"Good grief, boy. How'd you get to be so old and so dumb at the same time?"

"But everyone says..."

"Everyone ain't the Boss. Everyone is the *world*, and you know what kind of trouble thinkin' like the rest of the world can get you into. Besides, didn't you read that second lesson?"

"The one about the 'foolishness of God being wiser than the wisdom of men?'"

"Right! And the word of the cross bein' folly and so on?"

"So?"

"So that's what it's about!"

"Equality?"

"No, boy. Justice don't have nothin' to do with equality. It has to do with *forgiveness*! That's why God's justice appears foolish to the world. It don't make any sense in terms of equality and yin yang and goin' and comin' or whatever you said."

"Hand me another Shiner and explain."

"Okay," he said, tossing me a brown bottle. "Let me break this down for you."

"Thank you."

"The Boss tells you how to live life and you don't do it. He says to 'do justice, love mercy and walk humbly with your God.' And through Jesus He says to love God and yore neighbor as yoreself. Simple stuff, right?"

"Right."

"And do you do it?"

"Well, uh..."

"Heck no you don't do it. And what does God do

about that?"

"Well, uh..."

"He *forgives* you! That's what he does!"

"Okay..so..."

"So is *that* right and fair and equal and yin yang?"

"Well, no...uh...yes...uh...I don't know, Bubba. I'm only human!"

"That's just the *point*, boy! Of *course* you're human! You *cain't* be perfect. Even such a heavenly being as *I* am, almost ain't perfect."

I pointed to his pot belly. "What do you mean 'almost?'"

"Don't get personal. We were talkin' about *you*. And then the Boss gives you humans a great body and what do you do with it?"

"Uh...stuff it with fat and sugar, smoke our lungs out and dump in drugs from cocaine to coffee?"

"Right. Or you try to run the daylights out of it and call it 'exercisin.' If the body is the temple of the spirit y'all got some mighty interestin' spirits runnin' around down here."

"But..."

"And what does God do about that? He *forgives* you."

"But what about...?"

"Don't stop me now, boy, I'm on a roll." Bubba leaned closer to me and squinted his eyes. "God gives you an intellect capable of solving all the problems of the world - the ability to create computers that can almost think, the ability to feed the hungry of all nations, eradicate major diseases, live in cities in peace and harmony. And what do you do?"

"That's easy. We build armaments, play political games, hoard and squander resources, sue each other and destroy our internal and external environment so our cities are unlivable."

"Right! And what does God do about that? He *forgives* you! Good heavens, boy, God even sends Jesus to show you what God's like and you reject him, scourge him and nail him to a cross - and what does God do? He *forgives* you! That ain't *right* boy! That ain't the way the *world* does bidness. That ain't yin yang and goin' and comin' around and like that. That ain't even FAIR, for cryin' out loud."

"Then what is it?"

Bubba took a deep breath and smiled. "It's *God's justice*, boy! That's what it is. It's God's foolishness makin' the *world* look nuts. It's God talkin' to the alcoholic or the drug user or the plain ol' person on the street just tryin' to make a livin' or the troubled businessperson or you or even me and sayin' to us - 'LIGHTEN UP! I love you. This isn't all there is. There's more! Let me help. I forgive you. I love you. I even like you. You're not perfect. You cain't be. But you *are* forgiven. Get on with your life. Go out there and make some more mistakes. I'll laugh *at* you and I'll laugh *with* you. Of course life ain't fair. Of course it stinks sometimes. People get lousy deals, draw a bad card, cut the deck in an unfortunate place, cash in their chips too early, some of 'em ain't playin' with a full deck in the first place - that's just the way it is on Earth. So what? Stick with me,' God says. 'We'll ride this sucker out together and see where it goes to.'"

"I think I'm starting to get it."

"I hope so, boy. We're nearly out of beer and it's time to go out and get you back in that race, now that I wrote your story for you."

"I like God having a sense of humor."

"Yeah, so do I. I'd be in big trouble if God didn't. So would you. I just wish more of his people had one. It would help them out, especially those t.v. preachers. No sense of humor whatsoever. They're all sin, sickness and damnation. Don't know nothin' about forgiveness, mercy or humor - and that means they don't know nothin' about justice."

"Speaking of justice, how are you gonna get us back in the race," I said, getting up to head back to the road.

"We're gonna run it."

"Who's 'we' Cloud Breath? There's two thirds of the race to go and I'm already 30 minutes behind. If I have to wait for you I won't finish till next Wednesday."

"You got no faith, boy. That's yore problem. Now have I ever led you astray? Have I ever led you down the wrong path? Have I ever...?"

"Yes. Yes. And yes. Every time I meet up with you, you leave me in some horrible situation that takes days to talk myself out of."

Bubba got up and pulled me to my feet.

"Well, this time it's different, son. I'll get us back into that race." He winked. "Trust me." My stomach did a back flip.

At that point I knew I should have blown off the race and gone home. But I didn't. We went out to the road and started running. I was amazed that someone so overweight could go as fast as he could.

"I don't get it, Bubba. I'm here sweating my brains out and my bad knees are screaming for me to stop and you're jogging along there keeping right up with me just as though your feet aren't even touching the.....BUBBA!!!!" (I looked down and his feet were cycling in mid air.) "You're supposed to RUN, not FLY. That's not fair!!"

"Just testin' your sense of humor, boy. A lot like God's justice. Besides, I don't wear out near as many pair of shoes this way."

Suddenly Bubba headed off the road to the right along a cowpath.

"Where are you going now?" I asked. "The race is back down *that* road."

"Naw, the *official* race is back thataway. The short-cut is thisaway."

"*Shortcut*? Bubba! You can't take a shortcut! You have to stay on the road with everyone else! You have to follow the directions. You have to play by the same rules everyone else plays by. You have to..."

"Maybe *you* have to, boy. You forget..." he said, flying down the path with me at his heels. "...I'm an angel and you're a... you're a... you're a *mess*."

"But it's not fair!"

"Now wait just a minute here, son." Bubba turned around and I bumped right into his corpulent belly. "Watch where yore runnin'."

"Sorry."

"You keep hollerin' about 'fair.' You're not gonna get any farther ahead of where you would have anyway. Your talk with me took place in a kind of a time warp. And besides, are you runnin' this race for a trophy that the world gives out or are you runnin' it for the scenery and the fun?"

"Well, I..."

"You better be runnin' it for the fun and the journey, son. The end of the race is gonna come up too fast and too soon - if you get my meanin'."

"I'm afraid I do. But, Bubba..."

"But nothin.' Now hurry up or you'll mess up my timing."

"Are you sure you know where this thing comes out? It'd be awfully embarrassing if..."

Bubba glared back at me. "Boy, when are you gonna start trustin' me? I had this course scoped out a week ago. I know every inch of the race. I know every turn in this path through this high brush here.

Just stick with me."

Suddenly, we broke through the overgrowth and out onto the road. And there, not fifty feet away - was the finish line with all the race officials looking in our direction.

"Bubba!" I exclaimed. "You come back here and get me out of this!!"

As usual, the huge angel was nowhere to be found.

"They cain't see me, boy, and they cain't hear me either," a voice beside me said.

"Then make yourself visible, you big.."

"I *am* visible!" the race official said, stomping up to me with a rather unfriendly look on his face. "Just what do you think you're doing, young man?"

"Well, I... well there was this huge Texas angel named Bubba and..."

I heard muffled guffaws coming from the air behind me. "Forgot to tell you, boy," Bubba said to my ears only. "You start redefining justice and you're bound to get in trouble with the world."

"Well now's a fine time to let me in on your little secret!"

"What are you talking about?" the official said. "There are no secrets here. You know what the rules of this race are."

"No, not you - HIM!"

The man looked at the empty space behind me. Without taking his eyes off me, he smiled nervously and motioned to the EMS attendants at the finish line. As they came running toward us, I heard a knowing laugh from way up in the sky over my head.

"I cain't wait to hear you get out of this one, boy. I know you'll do it. You always do. Just remember, God's got a sense of humor and God'll forgive whatever it is you're thinkin' about me right now."

"BUBBA!!" I exclaimed as I took off in the opposite direction. I passed runners heading toward the finish line and noted their astonished looks as EMS attendants chased an obviously heat demented runner going the wrong way.

And I must admit, as I thought about the justice of God, I smiled.

Samuel 3:1-19

Now the boy Samuel was ministering to the Lord under Eli. And the word of the Lord was rare in those days; there was no frequent vision.

At that time Eli, whose eyesight had begun to grow dim, so that he could not see, was lying down in his own place; the lamp of God had not yet gone out, and Samuel was lying down within the temple of the Lord, where the ark of God was. Then the Lord called, "Samuel! Samuel!" and he said, "Here I am!" and ran to Eli, and said, "Here I am, for you called me." But he said, "I did not call; lie down again." So he went and lay down. And the Lord called again. "Samuel!" And Samuel arose and went to Eli, and said, "Here I am, for you called me." But he said, "I did not call, my son, lie down again." Now Samuel did not yet know the Lord, and the word of the Lord had not yet been revealed to him. And the Lord called Samuel again the third time. And he arose and went to Eli, and said, "Here I am, for you called me." Then Eli perceived that the Lord was calling the boy. Therefore Eli said to Samuel, "Go, lie down; and if he calls you, you shall say, 'Speak, Lord, for thy servant hears.'" So Samuel went and lay down in his place.

And the Lord came and stood forth, calling as at other times, "Samuel! Samuel!" And Samuel said, "Speak, for thy servant hears.." Then the Lord said to Samuel, "Behold, I am about to do a thing in Israel, at which the two ears of everyone that hears it will tingle. On that day I will fulfill against Eli all that I have spoken concerning his house, from beginning to end. And I tell him I am about to punish his house for ever, for the iniquity which he knew, because his sons were blaspheming God, and he did not restrain them. Therefore I swear to the house of Eli that the iniquity of Eli's house shall not be expiated by sacrifice or offering for ever."

Samuel lay until morning; then he opened the doors of the house of the Lord. And Samuel was afraid to tell the vision to Eli. But Eli called Samuel and said, "Samuel, my son." And he said, "Here I am." And Eli said, "What was it that he told you? Do not hide it from me. May God do so to you and more also, if you hide anything from me of all that he told you." So Samuel told him everything and hid nothing from him. And he said, "It is the Lord; let him do what seems good to him."

And Samuel grew, and the Lord was with him and let none of his words fall to the ground.

Bubba by Long Distance

(The following took place as I was about to give a sermon at St. David's Church in Austin. A cordless telephone sat on the free-standing altar behind me.)

My story tonight is a well thought out, erudite, carefully researched explication of the reading from the Old Testament, which is commonly referred to as "The Call of Samuel."

(Telephone rings.)

Excuse me a minute...Hello?? (Picking up the receiver and holding it to my ear.) Hey, who are you trying to kid? (Hang up.)

As I was saying, I want to talk about "The Call of Samuel."

(Phone rings again.)

I'm sorry. Excuse me....Hello...Listen lady, we're in the middle of a church service here, you know what I mean? And I don't have any time for crank phone calls about some angel on long distance! (Hang up.)

I'm really sorry. This has never happened to me before. Now, where was I?? Oh yes...the Old Testament lesson. Do you realize that Samuel didn't understand the first *three* times God called to him? Why....

(Phone rings third time.)

Hello!! Now listen here. You really must...What?? Come on...who is this really? I don't believe you. What do you mean - ask you the secret password. Okay. What's the secret password?......SHINER BOCK???!!! BUBBA—IT *IS* YOU!

Well what in the world are you doing *calling* me? You usually show up in person.....You're on the 127th floor of St. David's Hospital? But it only has five floors! Good grief! What happened?....You were watching the Cincinnati Bengals game last weekend from the top of the stadium and...your wings iced up and your halo got frostbite?? Oh, I see, your halo iced up and your wings got frostbite!!

I'm sorry to hear that. Hope you're getting treated well....Uh huh...Your only complaint is that Pastoral Care hasn't been around to see you yet? Okay, I'll send someone around tomorrow...Listen, nice talking to you but I've got a story to tell here and....What?...That's why you called?...You read my story?... Well, gee, that's real nice of you to call to congrat...That's not why you called?...There were some things I left out? Bubba, I didn't leave *anything* out...here, let me look at this a minute.

See...I start out telling them that Samuel's day was a day very much like our own. The word of the Lord was rare in those days and there was no frequent vision. Oh there are a lot of yahoos running around saying they have private access to the word of the Lord and claiming they know who's saved and who's not and when Jesus is coming back and what heaven looks like. But when you come right down to it the real word of the Lord is rare today, and there are no frequent visions. In fact we probably wouldn't know a vision if we tripped over it.

What? That's because we're not looking for them? Yeah, you're probably right, Bubba. I don't know though. That's the second thing I was going to tell them. I have always envied Samuel.

I know, I know. Envy's one of the biggies. I'm just being honest with you. I have always envied Samuel. I mean, here's this guy who's twelve years old and he gets this "call" from God. Suddenly he's got his life's profession laid out in front of him. Daggone that would make things easy! I never have understood this "call" business.

You...you haven't either...and what difference does it make anyway?

It makes a *lot* of difference, Bubba. I mean, you mention "call" to some people and they get all misty eyed and start drooling and fawning like you just said you were pregnant or something.

You...you've never been pregnant so you don't

know what that's like.

Well I haven't either but I also haven't received any divine telegrams or long distance phone calls, with the exception of yours of course. I mean, Samuel had it made! Here he gets a divine revelation straight from the Source. And some people think that that's what it takes to go into the ministry. They take this stuff literally and it gets real confusing for some of us who have never had that experience.

You think I...I wouldn't like it if did happen...because it would scare the daylights out of me. You're probably right. I think I'll mope along without that kind of call for the time being - hopefully forever. Well, what did you want to tell me that I left out?

We don't have that much time, Bubba. Make it quick so we can get home in time to catch 60 Minutes.

You'll.....give me the revised standard version..... Okay. Shoot.

Tell them....to watch their assumptions about what it means to be called. Both about who is called and to what. Yeah, that makes sense. Often we think only certain kinds of people are called to certain things. But here was Samuel, the custodian gofer of the temple, the one who opened the doors and kept the oil in the lamps - *he's* the one who gets called. So God frequently chooses people who are unlikely in society's eyes, even outcasts from society and the church, to do His will, right? Okay...what else?

Tell them....that the reason Samuel didn't click to who was calling him was because he wasn't *listening* for it. Oh, I see - it's God's job to call and our job to be willing to listen, to keep our channels open and to be attentive. I see. Okay.

Now what? Oh....tell them it is important to check the authenticity of the call as Eli did with Samuel. Eli asked what the vision had told Samuel and when he heard the authentic ring of it he said - "It *is* the Lord; let him do what seems good to him." Okay - so check the authenticity by sharing the experience with someone else in the community. It could be just the little voices in your own head talking, right?

Uh-huh...Next tell them this calling involves a *partnership* with God. Because after that encounter we're told Samuel grew and the Lord was with him and let none of his words fall to the ground empty. So to remember about the partnership and that God isn't sending you out alone to get clobbered by yourself. Okay...anything else?

The most important thing of all??? What's that???

Bubba!! I can't tell them THAT!!....We'll blow our cover as clergy. We'll no longer be able to...What? I see.... If *I* don't you will and that will mean another new roof on the church...uh-huh...okay...I'll tell them.

Here goes.....The "call" is *nothing special* or *sacred* or *different*. The call of God is in fact the most ordinary thing in the world. People are called by God every day in a variety of ways. Often, like Samuel, they don't hear the first few times because they're not attuned to it. But not to worry because God's call is like a broken record - if you don't hear it the first time it'll come around again in a little bit until you do, just like with Samuel.

The problem is what???....The problem is not that there are too *few* calls and too *few* visions, the problem is that there are too *many* competing for people's attention. That's why the other steps of watching assumptions and checking authority are so important - to make sure who's on the other end of the line!

Okay....that's pretty radical stuff but I'll tell them that God's call is *ordinary*. I'll bet that's another reason why people miss it - we keep expecting it to be something like Samuel's is reported to be and we don't even hear it through our friends, or kids, or something we read or see or think, huh?

Well, thanks an awful lot, Bubba. It was good to hear from you. I hope you get well soon.

You...you don't want to get well too soon because the nurses are all angels and...and...you can watch the game on t.v. next week instead of going up to freezin' yankee territory. I understand. Well it really was nice of you to call. I'll bet it cost you a lot of....what do you mean you *reversed* the charges!!! Bubba!!! Bubba!!! Don't hang up on me!!! BUBBA!!!

(Holds up quiet receiver.)

Well, I guess that's the final lesson. The call of God always involves a price. And we pay that price whether we accept the call like Samuel, or whether we choose, like so many people do, to refuse and (slams down receiver) hang up.

Ezekiel 31:1-6,10-14

In the eleventh year, in the third month, on the first day of the month, the word of the Lord came to me: "Son of man, say to Pharaoh king of Egypt and to his multitude:

"Whom are you like in your greatness?
Behold, I will liken you to a cedar in Lebanon,
with fair branches and forest shade, and of great height,
its top among the clouds.
The waters nourished it, the deep made it grow tall,
making its rivers flow round the place of its planting,
sending forth its streams to all the trees of the forest.
So it towered high above all the trees of the forest,
its boughs grew large and its branches long,
from abundant water in its shoots.
All the birds of the air made their nests in its boughs;
under its branches all the beasts of the field
brought forth their young;
and under its shadow dwelt all great nations.

"Therefore thus says the Lord God: Because it towered high and set its top among the clouds, and its heart was proud of its height, I will give it into the hand of a mighty one of the nations; he shall surely deal with it as its wickedness deserves. I have cast it out. Foreigners, the most terrible of the nations, will cut it down and leave it. On the mountains and in all the valleys its branches will fall, and its boughs will lie broken in all the watercourses of the land; and all the peoples of the earth will go from its shadow and leave it. Upon its ruin will dwell all the birds of the air, and upon its branches will be all the beasts of the field. All this is in order that no trees by the waters may grow to lofty height or set their tops among the clouds, and that no trees that drink water may reach up to them in height; for they are all given over to death, to the nether world among mortal men, with those who go down to the Pit."

Bubba and Blue Bell

My usual style in writing stories is to read through a Scripture passage a week or so ahead of time and then chew on it for a few days before putting anything on paper. That's just what I had done last Sunday afternoon, sitting on a lounge chair on the back porch drinking a cold one. I had just read through the passage from Ezekiel. I closed my eyes for a minute and was going over the first verse in my mind when....well let me replay for you what happened.

"In the eleventh year, in the third month, on the first day of the month, the word of the Lord came to me saying..."

"Son...flyin' around here in the Austin summer sure does make a heavenly body thirsty."

"BUBBA!!" I said, my eyelids flapping open to behold my favorite Texas angel sitting in the lawn chair next to me. "What are *you* doing here?"

"No questions answered till I get me a little somethin' to wet mah whistle, boy. Do I have to find it myself or are you gonna get it for me?"

"I'll get it, Bubba. What do you want - the usual?"

"The usual will do just fine, boy. Only thing that helps in the summer is to rent me a couple beers. Ya don't buy 'em ya know, ya just rent 'em, if ya know what I mean..."

He winked at me as I pulled a Shiner Longneck out of the cooler beside me.

"Love your summer outfit, Bubba. Where'd you get it, Woolworths?"

"Very funny, son. This is what you call 'Angel Chic.'"

"'Angel Chic'? You call wearing bullhide Tony Lama's, a white Stetson, burnt orange running shorts, and a green t-shirt with Save The Whales on it 'Angel Chic'?"

"You betcha, son. Now hand me that longneck and tell me yore problem."

"What makes you think I've got a problem?"

"'Cause if you didn't you'd be writin' a story instead of sittin' here jawin' with me."

"Okay, Bubba. Right as usual. It's about this Ezekiel passage. I..."

"Oh yes, Ezekiel. Crazy as a loon, he was. That's why I liked him so much. He saw stuff that wasn't there for the rest of us. The Boss showed him all kinds of stuff and then told him to go tell other people about it. Which passage has ya hung up, anyway?"

"It's the one about the tree. It really bothers me, Bubba."

"Really got ya *stumped*, huh? HAW, HAW, HAW."
I glared at him.

"Okay," he said. "The tree...the tree...OH YES, I remember now! The one that got too big for its branches...." He slapped his thigh and laughed.

"Cute, Bubba. Real cute. Yes that's the one. It's really scary!"

"What's scary about it?" he asked, taking a long swallow from the longneck.

"Well, here's this tree that is beyond compare. It was planted by God, nourished by God, it grew and provided a place for others to make their homes, it protected the weak and the young, it provided shelter and wisdom for multitudes and generations. And then something changed.

"The passage says '...its heart was proud of its height.' So God has it cut down. This once beautiful, lofty tree is now cut to the ground. It lies broken and abandoned, left to decay and ruin. And all those it formerly sheltered now leave it alone and go elsewhere because it has been abandoned by God and so no longer has meaning or use for them."

"You got the picture, son. But I still don't get what's so scary?"

"What's scary, Bubba, is that you can read Ezekiel's message in a number of ways."

"Oh, sure, I getcha. Sorta like fill-in-the-blanks with different things. Keep talkin, son, this is gettin' interestin'."

"That's right. For instance you could take out Pharaoh and put in the United States and the message would fit. Maybe our country is the tree Zeke is talking about, Bubba. We're certainly 'proud of our height.' And now we want to back up that tough guy pride with throwing our economic weight around the world instead of feeding the hungry, clothing the poor and setting the prisoners free."

"Yeah, yore right as rain about that, boy. The Boss is gettin' a mite worried about all this pride stuff. And you know what happens when He gets ticked!" He gestured with his free hand. "Down goes that tree!"

He pondered as he took another swallow. "And there are some other names you could fill in the blank with too ya know. Why you could put Argentina, Britain, Japan, Israel, Syria and Iraq in there. All that foolish nationalism swells up their hearts like a Luling watermelon, boy. And when that happens it's time for The Boss to come along and thump it."

"Now *that's* pretty scary, Bubba. But that's not the only way you could read the passage."

"I was wonderin' if you'd get around to this one, son."

"You're way ahead of me, Bubba, as usual. You see, you could also read that passage as referring to the *church*! We were planted and nurtured by God, just like everything in that passage says. And now we've built buildings and defined and proscribed and demanded and judged and decreed.

"I just wonder if the *church* isn't 'proud of *its* height' and so is being abandoned by those it used to shelter, due to lack of meaning and uselessness. I mean, isn't it horrifying to think of God cutting down the *church*?"

"Oh, I don't know, boy. Might be the best thing that ever happened to it. Wouldn't be the first time, either. Might sprout some new saplings that weren't quite so monolithic or enamored of their own majesty instead of being responsive to the One who planted them in the first place."

I looked at him strangely. "What did you say? 'Monolithic, enamored, responsive'? Those are pretty big words for you, Bubba."

"I know, boy, I know. I been practicin.' The Boss says we're gettin' too soft in the language department. So I been subscribin' to Reader's Digest and increasin' my word power.' Pretty impressive, ain't it." He pulled the latest rumpled issue out of his back pocket.

"Yes, it is. And that reminds me of another way of filling in the blanks in the story."

"Now don't go gettin' nasty with me, boy. Remember yore s'posed to respect yore elders and yore angels and I'm both!

"I ain't...I mean I'm not getting nasty. But it did just occur to me that we could put *your* name in there or *my* name in there or anybody we know's name in there and it would fit. And that's a *real* problem,

Bubba. Where does *pride* fit in to the Christian life? Ezekiel seems to be saying that any kind of pride is cut down and trampled into the dust.":

"No no no, boy. Ya got it all mixed up."

"Well unmix it for me, Bubba."

"I will in just a minute. First I got an important question for ya."

"What's that?"

"You got any Blue Bell ice cream to go with this beer?"

"Blue Bell and beer? YECH!"

"That's the trouble with you, boy. You ain't got no culture, no savoir fair, no coup de grass."

"I also ain't got no Blue Bell."

He gave me a dejected look. "That's a shame, son. I had a real hankerin' for some Cookies and Cream. Guess I'll just have to make this a short explanation and fly over to the H.E.B. store and get some on sale."

"I wish you would."

"Okay, now about this pride nonsense. People get that all messed up. The Boss don't have a problem with people feelin' prideful about their accomplishments. It's sorta like feelin' good and satisfied and enthused about a job well done."

"You mean about using their talents well and feeling good about that?"

"Right."

"But the problem, Bubba, is that that kind of pride

frequently leads to the other kind, and so Christians think they're not supposed to feel pride about *any-thing* - that it's un-Christian and God won't like it or will zap them for it, or cut them down like that tree of Ezekiel's."

"It ain't un-anything, boy. If ya get right down to it the Boss WANTS people to feel good about what they do with what He's given them. The point is to remember where the gifts *came* from in the first place, son. They ain't yore's to brag about but it's fine to feel good about usin' 'em and proud about how well you've exercised 'em."

"So it's okay to feel pride in ourselves and our accomplishments as long as we acknowledge the *source* of the talents and gifts."

"Now ya got it, son. That was the problem with Zeke's tree. And it's the same problem with nation-alism, denominationalism and anything else that tries to compete with the Boss. And He don't take too kindly to it, neither."

"So it's okay to branch out and be proud as long as you remember your roots?"

Bubba took the last swallow of his Shiner and stood up, handing me the empty bottle.

"That's right, boy, that's right. Now I don't mean to bark at ya, and I hope you don't get your fir up, but it's time for me to leave. Maple I'll see ya again if it's oak-a with you."

"Go eat your ice cream, Bubba."

As he stepped into the air and flew up over the house I called to him:

"Hey, Bubba — you forgot your Reader's Digest."

"That's okay, boy. You keep it. Maybe you'll find some words you can use in yore story. Then the Boss'll be proud of both of us."

"Wait a minute, Bubba!" I yelled. "You mean the Boss, I mean *God* feels *proud* about stuff?"

"Course He does, son! Back in Genesis He said 'It was good' didn't He? What do ya call that — embarrassment"

"I guess not." I looked up and waved. "Bye, Bubba."

He waved back. "Bye, son. Keep that Shiner on ice, cause ya never know..."

He flew off in the direction of the H.E.B. store. I wandered back to my lawn chair, closed my eyes again, thought about all he had said, and imagined him *proudly* digging into a huge mound of Cookies and Cream - but only *after* he gave thanks to the Boss.

Isaiah 53.4-12

Surely he has borne our griefs and carried our sorrows; yet we esteemed him stricken, smitten by God, and afflicted. But he was wounded for our transgressions, he was bruised for our iniquities; upon him was the chastisement that made us whole, and with his stripes we are healed.

All we like sheep have gone astray; we have turned every one to his own way; and the Lord has laid on him the iniquity of us all. He was oppressed, and he was afflicted, yet he opened not his mouth; like a lamb that is led to the slaughter, and like a sheep that before its shearers is dumb, so he opened not his mouth.

By oppression and judgment he was taken away; and as for his generation, who considered that he was cut off out of the land of the living, stricken for the transgression of my people? And they made his grave with the wicked and with a rich man in his death, although he had done no violence, and there was no deceit in his mouth. Yet it was the will of the Lord to bruise him; he has put him to grief; when he makes himself an offering for sin, he shall see his offspring, he shall prolong his days; the will of the Lord shall prosper in his hand; he shall see the fruit of the travail of his soul and be satisfied; by his knowledge shall the righteous one, my servant, make many to be accounted righteous; and he shall bear their iniquities.

Therefore I will divide him a portion with the great, and he shall divide the spoil with the strong; because he poured out his soul to death, and was numbered with the transgressors; yet he bore the sin of many, and made intercession for the transgressors.

Bubba and Deb

I was sitting on a plane from Atlanta to Austin last weekend, returning from a conference and from visiting some old friends who had been quite close to my first wife and me. I was feeling pretty sad and teary about her sudden death and had been gazing out the window so no one would see me cry. The seat next to me was, fortunately, empty. I pressed the little button in the armrest to recline the seat and closed my eyes to rest.

I had just gotten comfortable and settled in when I heard a familiar voice:

"S'cuse me, son. but could ya pass the peanuts?"

My eyes shot open and I nearly got whiplash turning my neck.

"BUBBA!" I said, with much surprise and shock and welcome. He was dressed in his usual orange outfit with his wings slung over the back of the seat.

"What're you...How did you...?"

"Oh, I was in the neighborhood and I saw ya

flyin' by so I thought I'd just see if Delta was ready when I was."

"Apparently so. Here comes the stewardess to take your order." I closed my eyes and turned my head. "I don't think I can watch this."

"We'd like Shiner Bocks and water, ma'am."

"Yes sir, right away."

I cautiously opened my eyes. "Bubba, she didn't say a *thing* about you being here...looking like *that*. How'd you do it?"

"Just an old trick I learned from Obe Wan Kenobe."

The stewardess returned.

"Now pay the lady, boy. I didn't bring any foldin' money with me."

I shelled out the cash and we sat in silence, looking straight ahead for a long time, hearing only the hum of the engines. Bubba broke the quiet.

"I heard...I say I heard ya had a mite o' trouble, son."

"More than a mite, Bubba. Deb died."

"Like havin' yore heart tore outta ya, ain't it, son."

"More like having your *soul* torn out, Bubba."

"Hmmmmmmmmmm." Bubba murmured, drinking his Shiner.

"'Hmmmmmmmmmm' *what*?" I asked.

"I was just wonderin.' Why do you suppose the Boss lets that happen?"

"You're asking *me*? *You're* supposed to know all

that, aren't you?"

"Hey, boy, I'm only an angel! Just because I been around a few thousand years don't mean I know it *all* - not yet anyhow. I don't know as how I'll *ever* figure the Boss out. So I was wonderin' how you see it that he lets things like yore wife's death happen."

"Simple, Bubba. It's because he's *not* the Boss."

"Now hold on there, boy!" He bolted up. "If yore gonna talk like that, I'm gonna move over a seat or two so's I don't get zapped when the lightnin' hits."

I put my hand on his arm. "Sit down, Bubba, sit down. What I mean is, God's not the Boss in terms of arranging for Deb to die. God didn't set it up. God didn't want it to happen. God didn't take her from me. It was not God's will. There was no divine purpose in her dying to serve some innocuous or insidious eternal plan prearranged to make us pawns - in spite of some of the things some allegedly religious people have told me without asking whether or not I wanted to hear their opinion."

"I s'pose folks *have* been tellin' you some strange stuff. Like it was 'Gawd's will,' or 'There's a reason for ever-thing' and the like."

"You got *that* right, Bubba. And I just don't believe it. God isn't vicious or mean or vindictive. God didn't kill her so some ridiculous plan could be fulfilled. I just don't believe it."

"I think yore right, son. I never have understood

why you humans have to have an explanation for everything and when you can't find one you make up some silly thing that doesn't have anything to do with the way things really are."

He held up his empty glass. "Do you think we might could get that stewardess to get us a couple more o' them Shiners?"

The stewardess appeared out of nowhere with two more bottles.

Bubba looked at her. "Put it on his tab, ma'am." She nodded and walked away, slightly dazed. "Now, like I was sayin.' What was I sayin' anyway, son? Oh yes, I was sayin' about makin' up explanations instead of just seein' things as they are.

"I agree, Bubba."

"Well, then, what *do* you believe, boy? If the Boss ain't the Boss, then how does the Boss fit into all this?"

I paused for a moment, then said: "Helplessness, Bubba."

"Oh sure, son, that's it. Helplessness." He raised his drink, then turned his face to mine. "Say *what*? 'Helplessness'? You better explain yoreself."

"Just like the scripture says, Bubba. God's weakness is with us always. God's weakness is our strength. God was as helpless to do anything about Deb's sickness and death as I was - as the doctors were. God was, in fact, as helpless as Deb was. God couldn't fix it. God couldn't change it. God didn't want it.

"The only thing God could do was to suffer with us, to mourn with us the ending of a loving young life, to endure with us the sadness of a painful, wrenching breaking of a couple, to rage with us at the strongly felt unfairness of our finitude, to cry with us and mourn the loss of one so loved and lovely."

Bubba said quietly: "I...I think I see what ya mean, son."

"For me, Bubba, that's a lot more real than a far off God who makes capricious plans and remains unaffected by our feelings. And for me.....that's enough."

Bubba opened another small bag of peanuts, chomped on them a while, then said: "Do ya mind, I say, do ya mind if I ask ya one more question, boy?"

"I guess not, depending on what it is."

"Well, no offense, ya understand, but...well...as a human what's most helpful to ya in gettin' through this?"

"That's easy," I said. "Three things. First, we had no regrets. We didn't put off doing things. We did them when we wanted to. We were protective of our time together and didn't let anyone else take precedence over it. We spent all the time we could together and enjoyed each other's company, and we went places and did things here and now, not waiting till later and making excuses.

"The second thing I've already told you - there

was no reason or purpose for Deb's death. God did not plan or want it. God accepted it with the same helplessness, anger, and sadness as the rest of us. And third is the loving support I've received from friends and acquaintances here and elsewhere."

"I can tell ya too, son, there's a whole passle o' angels concerned about you and those who knew her. Course *I'm* the *main* one, ya know!"

"I know, Bubba." I smiled.

There was another long silence between us.

"Bubba?" I asked.

"Yes, son - I know what you want. I was wonderin' when you'd get around to askin.' All I can tell ya is that she's bein' looked after real good and that she's as much a gift to us as she was to you."

Bubba reached over and squeezed my hand. A tear slid slowly down his cheek. And then, as silently as he appeared - he vanished, leaving me alone with the steady droning hum of the engine.

Genesis 32.24-29

And Jacob was left alone; and a man wrestled with him until the breaking of the day. When the man saw that he did not prevail against Jacob, he touched the hollow of his thigh; and Jacob's thigh was put out of joint as he wrestled with him. Then he said, "Let me go, for the day is breaking." But Jacob said, "I will not let you go, unless you bless me." And he said to him, "What is your name?" And he said, "Jacob." Then he said, "Your name shall no more be called Jacob, but Israel, for you have striven with God and with men, and have prevailed.

Then Jacob asked him, "Tell me, I pray, your name." But he said "Why is it that you ask my name?" And there he blessed him.

Bubba in Genesis

It had been a lousy week. Too many deaths at the hospital, too many hours at work, not enough time alone, too much time alone, grieving about the past, apprehensive about the future, conflicted about the present. I was ruminating about my dilemmas Saturday morning as I stood in my running shorts washing the car in the driveway. To tell the truth, I was grumbling about doing it alone, complaining to no one in particular about the unfairness of my wife's death, feeling angry, frustrated and generally unpleasant. As I bent over to get some tar off the bottom of the driver's door I was startled by a familiar voice.

"Oh, it ain't as bad as all that, boy!"

"BUBBA!!" I raised up, hitting my head on the side mirror. "God..."

"'Bless' it, son. Bless it!"

"Yeah, that too." I moaned, closing my eyes and holding the swelling bump. "What're *you* doing here?"

"Fine way to greet an angel, boy. Open them beady eyes of yores and you'll see."

I squinted my eyes open to see a 250 pound angel wearing an orange tank suit and flexing his biceps.

"I think my brain's damaged, Bubba. You look like 50 pounds of potatoes in a 20 pound sack."

"Well you ain't exactly Arnold Schwarzenneger ya know."

"What're you wearing that get-up for? Hallowe'en's two weeks off."

"Very funny. Verrry funny. Here I am tryin' to help you out and you make bad jokes."

"Help me out? If you want to help me out grab a rag and wash these dirty windows," I said, disappearing around the other side of the car.

"Boy, don't you know angels don't do windows? Ain't in our contract. Nope, I'm here to help you with yore sermon."

"My sermon? What's that outfit got to do with...?"

"What's the scripture, son?" he said, flexing his husky wrists.

"I don't know," I yelled from behind the rear fender. "Some weird thing about Jacob wrestling with an......" I stood up and peered over the car at a grinning, flexing Bubba. "Oh no...," I whispered. "Not *you*?"

"Whaddaya mean 'Not me?' Of *course* it was me. Who else would the Boss send on such an important mission?"

"Well, there's...."

"Don't answer that, boy. Just hush up and let me tell ya about it."

"I knew you would."

"Course I could use somethin' to keep my throat cool."

"Hot story, huh? Help yourself to the cooler. And get one for me. I have a feeling I'll need it."

We leaned against the car with our bottles of Shiner and he began.

"The Boss had me following Jacob for some time. I mean, that boy was crafty. Course you don't have to be too crafty when yore brother's a space cadet and yore daddy's near blind and dyin'."

"Bubba!!"

"Just tellin' it like it was, boy. Esau sold his birthright - land, cattle, money, the whole shootin' match - to Jacob for a bowl of soup. Not even Texas chili! And would you believe Esau's descendants went on to found some big university here in College Station?"

"Bubba!!"

"Don't interrupt me, son, I'm on a roll," he said, taking a big swallow. "Then Jacob dresses up in Esau's clothing and cheats Esau out their blind, dyin' father's blessing."

"This is better than 'Dallas' used to be!" I said. "What happened next.?"

"Then Jacob turns tail and runs."

"And Esau follows?"

"Not yet. It takes a while for the boy to realize he's been had, and get a burr under his saddle. In the meantime, Jacob takes two wives, cheats his new daddy-in-law out of his cattle and runs away again. When his daddy-in-law Laban catches up with him somewhere around Blanco, Jacob makes it seem like it was Laban's fault and makes a peace treaty with him."

"Just like J.R.!"

"You get the picture, son. Esau and Bobby Ewing had a lot in common. So there's Jacob, feelin' fat and sassy with himself for pullin' off another deal, when somebody rides in to tell him Esau is on his way with 400 cadets from the Corps!"

"I'll bet that shook him."

"Nope. Just like J.R., he divides his flocks and herds and folks into two groups so even if he loses one he's still got the other. Next he sends a Lexus, a Rolex, and 401 tickets to the Super Bowl on ahead to his brother to try to buy him off. Then, just like they used to freeze-frame J.R. sittin' back in his leather chair with that smirk on his face, Jacob sits back on his blanket, alone in the camp, and waits."

"And that's where you came in," I said, opening another one for myself.

"Right. I mean, I was ready for the boy. I had been doin' two-a-day work outs. I knew what I was up against. That Jacob was a big-un. A hunk."

"But why did the Boss, uh, I mean God want you to *wrestle* with him, Bubba?"

"Good heavens, son, that's the point! The Boss *wants y'all* to rassle with him. That's the trouble with the church, boy. Makes your relationship with him seem about as exciting as a coffee hour. The Boss wants you to get your hands dirty, get some calluses on 'em, build up yore strength by going a few rounds with him. Dig in, grab hold, grapple, argue, sweat and swear a little with him."

"But Bubba..."

"What's the matter, son? Think the Boss cain't take it? Why, the Boss is in even better shape than *I* am."

I looked at Bubba's bulging belly and said, "I hope so."

"What was that, boy?"

"I said, 'I'll bet he is.'"

"That was Jacob's problem, ya know."

"He was out of shape?"

"He was out of shape with the Boss. But Jacob thought he was in *great* shape. He thought he was crafty and slick and smooth and fast. That was his image of himself. He thought the only way he deserved to get ahead was by trickery and stealing. That was his identity, son. That's who he thought he was. That was the name he called himself by. When he looked in the mirror every morning that was who he saw."

"So, still, why wrestle with him?"

"He didn't want to let loose of his old identity, boy. I dang near had to cripple the sucker to get him to cut loose of it. I mean, he was attached to it like stink on a skunk - the way most people are."

"I can understand that, Bubba. Even though an old identity's painful, it's a lot more comfortable - maybe even enjoyable - than taking on a new one."

"Well, we rassled all night long until morning. I mean, we went for broke. We kicked and grunted and grabbed and hollered and swat (that's past tense of 'sweat,' boy) and tore and twisted till the sun rose. I had a great time. Course I was a mite younger then, and I enjoyed that stuff more. It's not that he was beatin' me ya know, just that I was gettin' hungry for some grits and Elgin sausage and I wanted to leave. And he was bound and determined not to let me."

"So you cheated."

Bubba stood back with his hands on his hips. "How dare you even imply such a thing," he said. "I didn't cheat. Angels never cheat, boy. I just used the old 'thigh out of joint' move on him. Works time. Then I delivered the message."

"What message?"

"The one the Boss sent me to tell him, son. His new name. His new identity."

"That's why you wrestled with him?"

"That's why he wrestled with me and with himself. He wouldn't give it up until he'd wrestled and fought through the dark of the night. It wasn't until he was all pooped out that he'd even listen to it - much less have his defenses down and accept it."

"Then he asked you your name."

Bubba groaned. "Yeah, and I got misquoted again. I didn't say 'Why are you askin' me?'"

"What *did* you say?"

"I said 'Shut yore face, camel breath, it ain't none of your business.'"

"I can see why they left it out. Why didn't you tell him your name?"

"Boy, can you imagine the problems we'd have if you found the name 'Bubba' in the Book of Genesis?"

"It *would* take some explaining. So what happened to Jacob?"

"The boy did just fine. He took that new identity and ran with it. All he needed was a new name. And the Boss's got millions of 'em."

"Really?"

"Yep. Got one for everybody in that church yore talkin' to Sunday."

"You're kidding."

"Nope. All they gotta do is risk the wrestling to get it. You included."

I put my beer bottle down and walked away from him. "I don't want one," I said.

"Been meanin' to talk to you about that, boy. Where you runnin' off to? You ain't chicken are ya?"

"Back off, buzzard wings. I'm not going to fight with you. Leave me alone. I'm doing just fine."

"Yeah, sure you are. Well the Boss says different. He sent me with a little somethin' to tell ya, so..."

I whirled around and before he could speak I grabbed the garden hose and squirted him full blast in the face with water. Then I ran.

"You cain't outrun my wings, son," he said, flying over the car and tackling me on the lawn. I felt like I'd been landed on by a king sized waterbed.

"Let me go," I hollered. "I don't want to hurt you."

"That's what I like about you, boy," Bubba laughed. "You're an optimist."

"Okay, Bubba - you asked for it."

"Do yore worst, son!" Bubba replied. And we started.

Grass, chiggers, fire ants and tree limbs filled the ball of dusty air around us as we hollered, grabbed, twisted and grappled on the ground. I have no recall of how long we struggled there. It was strange. Clearly Bubba was not trying to overcome me. He merely wanted to contain me, and he did. It was almost like fighting against myself. Finally I felt exhausted and fell back, gulping air, with Bubba sitting on my chest.

"You ready to hear that name now, boy?"

"Yes, yes. Anything to get you off of me."

"Well," he said, cupping his hands and starting to whisper in my ear, "here it is."

I listened, then, with a burst of energy grabbed his arms and pushed with my knees, flipping him over my head.

"I don't want *that* one!" I yelled, and started to run again. But Bubba didn't move. He just lay there, his eyes closed, his chest not moving.

"Bubba?" I stopped and turned around. "Bubba, are you alright?" He still was not breathing. I cautiously walked back to him, kneeled down and shook him in CPR fashion. It was like shaking a huge bowl of orange Jell-O.

"Bubba! Bubba! Are you all right?"

One eye opened, a smile crossed his face and he grabbed me. "Gotcha," he said. "The old, 'hold your breath trick' fools 'em every time," he yelled. And we were at it again.

"Better calm down, son, you're gonna bust somethin'," Bubba said as we rolled around and around, kicking and struggling. "Yore a better rassler than I thought," he said. "So I'm gonna have to do somethin' I hadn't counted on."

"NO! NOT THAT!" I yelled, as my thigh went out of joint and I stopped moving, thoroughly exhausted, bruised and done.

Bubba leaned down once again to whisper. "Now, son, here it is."

I heard it clearly this time, knowing all along what it must be, as each one of us knows God's name and identity for us when we're honest about it. I laid there a while, catching my breath, letting the name and identity sweep over and through me, healing past memories, suturing wounds, filling dark future with searing light.

Slowly I raised my bruised body and stood to find Bubba gone. I assessed the bodily damage, found it to be minimal and my hip relatively back in place. As I looked up I noticed a piece of paper flapping under the windshield wiper of the car. I limped over to remove it. It was in a funny scrawl and it read:

> "Nice job, son. Ya done good. I ain't had that much fun in a long time. Sorry to up and leave but it was gettin' past my lunch time. Remember that name. It'll take you where you want to go, or at least where the Boss wants you to go. And remember to tell all them people on Sunday that the Boss has got a new name for each one of them — whenever they're ready to rassle. Tell 'em to be lookin' for me, or somebody like me anyway.
>
> Happy Trails,
> Bubba
>
> P.S. You'll find that cooler o' yores empty, boy. I took the extras with me. I figgered I earned 'em."

Luke 2.8-14

And in that region there were shepherds out in the field, keeping watch over their flock by night. And an angel of the Lord appeared to them, and the glory of the Lord shone around them, and they were filled with fear. And the angel said to them, "Be not afraid; for behold, I bring you good news of a great joy which will come to all the people; for to you is born this day in the city of David a Savior, who is Christ the Lord. And this will be a sign for you: you will find a babe wrapped in swaddling cloths and lying in a manger." And suddenly there was with the angel a multitude of the heavenly host praising God and saying, "Glory to God in the highest, and on earth peace among people."

Bubba in Bethlehem

Very late, one cold night on a hillside overlooking the quiet little town of Bethlehem, a shepherd boy named Aaron tossed another twig onto a burning campfire. He was about ten years old - and he was worried.

His Mama and Papa were in the next village helping a sick relative. They would be gone all night. There was no one else to watch the flock of sheep but him, and he was all alone.

Well, not quite **all** alone. There were the twenty-five sheep, and the dog who sat, with its head on its paws, watching for any movements or sounds. And then — he glanced to the side of the campfire — there was his little sister, Karin.

Karin was five years old, and into everything — except sitting still. She needed a separate sheep dog for herself, Aaron thought, as he sighed a deep sigh and wondered how he would make it through the night. Her big dark eyes looked over at him, and the moon shone down on her long black hair.

"Okay, okay. You're cute and we both know it." He walked over and sat down beside her on the blanket in front of the fire. "But we have to stay very close together tonight, Karin. We have to watch these sheep and not let any get away, or..." he said, looking out over the hillside, "...not let any be eaten by wolves.."

"WOLVES!?"

"Yes, Karin! Wolves!" That got her attention, he thought. "Huge, vicious animals with teeth like this...." He opened his mouth wide and bared his teeth and growled. The dog raised its head inquisitively. Karin bit her quivering lip and seemed about to cry.

"But don't you worry, little sister," he said, putting his arm around her and smiling. "As long as you stick next to me everything will be fine."

"I'll...I'll be right...*here!*" She snuggled closer to her older brother. "Just don't leave me alo..."

At that moment the dog stood up but kept perfectly still.

"What is it, boy?" Aaron asked. He knew the well-trained sheep dog had detected some movement in the flock. "What do you hear?"

Just then the sheep broke out in a noisy bleating, and the dog ran off to the far side of the flock.

"What is it?" Karin asked.

"Could be a wolf, or it could just be they got spooked by their own shadows. Sheep are pretty dumb, you know." He stood and glanced in the direction of the noise. "I'd better go check." He pointed to the fire. "You stay here and keep the fire going."

"But what if...?"

"Just don't run off, Karin. You got that?"

"Uh-huh," she said, unconvincingly.

"I'll be right back," her brother said, and he disappeared into the darkness.

Karin sat looking back and forth with her eyes but not moving her head. She didn't like being left behind again. She was big enough to help. And she wasn't afraid of any old wolves, either.

The fire popped and she jumped to her feet. Well, not *too* afraid, anyway.

Just then she heard a strange flapping noise behind her. Her little heart nearly beat through her chest. She was afraid to turn around and afraid not to. When the flapping stopped, she slowly turned and looked up, not believing her wide open eyes.

There in front of her stood a six foot creature with wings and a scowl on its face.

"Where are your parents, kid?" the thing said.

"Whaaaa...What...did...did you...say...?"

"Are you deaf, child? I said: 'Where are your parents?' Your folks. Big People. You savvy?"

"They're not...here." She started trembling and the edges of her little mouth started to pull down. "What...*are*...you?"

"Oh, good grief. Don't go cryin' on me, darlin.' I cain't take a female in tears." The huge creature walked over and knelt down next to her. "I'm an angel, kid. You heard of angels, haven't ya?"

"Well, yes. I think so." She pointed to his back. "Are those...wings?"

"I'm afraid so." The angel looked around, then back at the wide-eyed child. "Now, lissen here, kid. I was supposed to meet your parents at this spot and give them some news..."

"What's...your...name?"

The angel looked at her with a smirk. He held out his weathered hand. "Bubba," he said. "What's yours?"

She put her tiny hand in his. "Karin," she said. "Bubba's a funny name. Where did you come from? Heaven?"

"Close, child. Texas. It hasn't been invented yet, but..."

"And what are those?" She pointed to his feet.

"Tony Lama Bullhides, darlin.' You cain't get 'em in Jerusalem."

"No. I mean those." She pointed to his heels."

"Spurs. But I didn't come here for no fashion show. I'm supposed to tell your folks that...wait a minute here..." Bubba fumbled inside his white jump suit and took out a slip of paper. "Here it is..." He cleared his throat. "Be not afraid." He looked at her. "I guess we already covered that, didn't we?"

She smiled at him.

"Okay, uh...Behold! I bring you good news of a great joy which will come to all the people; for to you is born this day in the City of David a saviour, who is Christ the Lord. And this will be a sign for you; you will find a babe wrapped in swaddling cloths and lying in a manger. And the baby's name is Jesus."

"You did that real good," she said, smiling up at him.

"Thanks. Some ol' boy name of Luke's gonna write it all down later."

"I can't read yet. But my brother's trying to teach me. He..."

"Yore brother? Where's *he* at?" Bubba scowled.

"He's checking on the sheep..."

"Well, let me go git him and then I can read this to him and git on my rounds."

Bubba stood and slowly rose from the ground into the air.

"I see him. You stay here, Karin. We'll be right back."

No sooner had Bubba disappeared from sight than Karin started thinking.

"Bethlehem isn't far off," she thought. "I wonder if I could find that Saviour-baby Jesus. I'd sure like to take him something for his birthday." She felt the rough blanket around her shoulders. "Maybe he could use this blanket to keep warm tonight!"

Karin carefully arranged some stones in front of the fire. Then she ran into the night in the direction of Bethlehem.

The dog barked menacingly at Bubba's descending Tony Lama's.

"Git holt of that critter, boy!" he hollered at the frozen Aaron.

Aaron stood stark still watching the huge creature come down through the air. He didn't know whether to run or attack. Fortunately, his wobbly legs would do neither. But he did call off the dog.

"Here, boy." The dog came to him and Aaron held it by the collar. "But if you give me any trouble, mister, I let the dog go. And he's a killer."

Bubba looked up to the sky, muttering, "Kids and dogs. I cain't believe the Boss *did* this to me..." He eyed the boy warily. "Hang on to that mutt, kid, and lissen up. I need to make this fast. Name's Bubba. I hail from Texas. These here are boots and spurs. Forget about tryin' to understand that. Just lissen to the message. 'Unto you is born....'"

"You're a little late, mister. I already know *that*."

"What? How could you...?"

"I just helped that sheep over there give birth to that baby lamb."

Bubba looked at the tiny lamb bleating in the darkness.

"That's right cute, son. But it ain't what I had in mind, exactly. As I was tellin' yore sister..."

"Omigawsh," Aaron said. "I nearly forgot about her. I'd better get back to the campfire before she..."

"Just a second boy. Let me check." Bubba rose high in the sky, then drifted back down. "We're in trouble, kid. She's gone. But she did leave a bunch of stones in the shape of an arrow — and it pointed toward Bethlehem."

Aaron sat down on a rock with his head in his hands. The dog, understanding, licked his face. "They'll kill me. My parents will kill me."

Bubba looked at the dejected child. "And the Boss'll banish me to Cleveland if I don't get all my announcin' done. But what the heck. Okay, son. Tell that dog there to watch the sheeps." He reached out his huge hand. "Then climb aboard and we'll see can we find her."

Seconds later Bubba and Aaron were gliding through the air. A giant silver moon gleamed over the earth and a huge shining star stood still in the sky over a certain part of the town.

"That's the biggest star I ever saw!" Aaron said, pointing above them.

"And the biggest one you ever *will* see, son," Bubba replied. "It's the one that stands over the stable where the Saviour-baby Jesus is sleepin'."

"That's IT, Bubba! Go down there! That's where Karin is! I just *know* it!"

"Well, okay. If you say so. But...," he pointed far ahead, "...if it was up to me I'd check out that circus over there on the outskirts of town first..."

The two slowly moved over Bethlehem and hovered over the stable.

"I don't see her, boy."

"Let's go down and look inside. I still bet she's in there!" Aaron said, as they softly landed outside the stable door and carefully opened it.

The huge angel and the little boy walked hand in hand toward the farthest stall, where animals were gathered around the young couple trying to keep warm in the hay. There, snuggled against a donkey, was Karin, half asleep. Her droopy eyes were glued to the little baby wrapped in her own woolen blanket.

Aaron sat beside her, put his arm around her, and looked and looked.

"He didn't have a blanket," Karin said, "...so I gave him mine."

"That was a right nice thing to do, little lady," Bubba said. "But we've got to get you home now. Your parents will be looking for you..."

"Oh, no, Bubba," Aaron said. "They're not coming back till..."

"Trust me, boy. They'll be home tonight."

Karin looked at him. "But how do you know...?"

"I'm an *angel*, remember! It's my **job** to know." He picked them both up in his arms, winked at the couple and the baby in the manger, and floated out through an open loft at the top of the barn.

As they flew across the sky with the moon at their back, Aaron asked: "Just what is a Saviour-baby, Bubba?"

Bubba hesitated a second and said: "It's a baby who grows up to love us more than we do ourselves, forgive us more than we do ourselves, want more for us than we want for ourselves." He looked down at the nodding Karin. "It's a baby who grows up to accept our strength and to know our weaknesses; a baby who grows up to be an adult who loves enough to die to change the world through us, if we'll let him."

Aaron looked back at the stable in the distance. "Gee, I'd like to help him."

"That's all he asks, son, is to give it yore best shot." Bubba hugged the two children. "And to love one another."

A silence came over them as they slowly descended by the campfire. Karin woke up in time to say goodbye to Bubba as he floated up out of sight.

"Now y'all be good, and remember to tell your parents what I told you!" He looked over the hill. "They'll be here in a few minutes."

The brother and sister waved until they could see him no more. Just then, their Mama and Papa came into sight, carrying the baby lamb that Aaron had helped with earlier.

"Mama! Papa!" the two yelled. "We saw an angel and went to Bethlehem, and Karin gave the Saviour-baby Jesus her wool blanket...and..."

Their stunned parents sat them down with the lamb by the fire and listened patiently as the excited children told their story. They hugged the children close and uttered a prayer for their safety, no matter what had really happened. Then they put down some soft blankets and covered Aaron and Karin to go to sleep.

Aaron, struggling against drowsiness, poked his sister lying next to him. "What will we call the new lamb, Karin?"

A long pause followed. Then her soft, sleepy voice whispered: "Texas."

Their father, overhearing their talk, asked: "What's a 'Texas'?"

A small speck passed in front of the great star in the heavens, as Karin replied: "It hasn't...been invented...yet." And the children were sure they heard the flapping of wings far away.

And that is why we still, to this very day, put angels with little tiny boots on them on top of our Christmas trees, to remind us all of the wonderful news of Jesus' birth, as told to the shepherds by Bubba in Bethlehem.

Mark 6.45-52

Immediately after the feeding of the five thousand, Jesus made his disciples get into the boat and go before him to the other side, to Bethsaida, while he dismissed the crowd. And after he had taken leave of them, he went up on the mountain to pray. And when evening came, the boat was out on the sea, and he was alone on the land. And he saw that they were making headway painfully, for the wind was against them.

And about the fourth watch of the night he came to them, walking on the sea. He meant to pass by them, but when they saw him walking on the sea they thought it was a ghost, and cried out; for they all saw him, and were terrified. But immediately he spoke to them and said, "Take heart, it is I; have no fear." And he got into the boat with them and the wind ceased. And they were utterly astounded, for they did not understand about the loaves, but their hearts were hardened.

Beach Blanket Bubba

I was lying on the beach in Mexico under the shade of a large umbrella. Before me the light blue waves steadily rolled in, pounding against the white sand. Behind me obnoxious strains of elevator music blared from the sunken bar up at the hotel. In my lap was the Scripture passage for today, which I had perused for nearly one hour and two cervezas.

And in my head I was cursing Father Gervais.

"Children's story?!" I said to his imaginary form, complete with clerical collar wringing his neck. "You changed the rules without telling me! You got me to agree to do this service and THEN you told me - by letter no less - that it was a CHILDREN'S SERMON!! Dirty pool! Foul play! Balk! Footfault! Clipping!"

I was not ready for this! I did not have children, I did not spend time around children and thus did not speak their esoteric language. When it comes to small human beings, I have been characterized - quite unjustly I might add - as being a little to the right of W.C. Fields.

And now, Father Gervais of St. Richard's of Round Rock had set me up to do a Children's Story in his vacationing absence.

Indeed.

And of all passages, the one before me lent itself to a children's story not a whit.

I tossed the passage aside, thinking some contemplation on the waves - and possibly another cerveza - would bring inspiration, or at least sleep. And I was ready for either.

But as I stared out over the ocean, something, some speck of movement far away on the horizon caught my attention. At first it was a large dot on the sea. As it got closer, it got bigger and I could see it was orange in color.

It looked like a very large person, or a very large water balloon, heading directly for me - and walking across the water. I rubbed my eyes and vowed no more cerveza for that day. Then, as the object got closer, something began to look vaguely familiar to me. It was the cowboy hat.

As he stepped onto the shore and walked over to me I stood and stared at him.

"BUBBA!!!" I yelled. "What are *you* doing here?"

"Well, I shore am glad to see you too, boy! You always do offer me such warm greetings."

"Oh! Sorry, Bubba. You just surprised me, is all."

"I *always* surprise you, son! Part of what bein' a angel is all about! Surprisin' people."

He eyed the beer in the sand by my beach towel.

"And the other part is havin' people be hospitable to ya. So why don't you order me one of those things and let's talk."

I signaled the waiter and he sleepily brought over two more Coronas. Nobody there was in a hurry.

"Can he see you?" I asked, when the man had left.

"Not unless I want him to," Bubba replied. "And right now I don't want him to...'cause one look at these here wings and they'd never let you out of this country - think you were a saint or something, talkin' with angels." He sat his huge frame down on the other towel. "'Sides that, they'd start accusin' me of doin' miracles and stuff."

I looked at him and pointed out to the horizon. "Like walking on the water?"

Bubba smiled. "Did ya like that, boy? I did that for *yore* benefit."

"What?"

"Well I happened to be in the area here and was sorta listenin' in on yore thoughts, and..."

"BUBBA!" I bolted up, as two women in tiny swimsuits jogged by us. "You can listen in on my THOUGHTS?! — ALL of them?"

"No, boy. Not ALL of them. That'd be too borin'." He laid back on the towel, looking something like a beached whale with wings. "I only listen in when you've got that worried look on yore face - which, by the way, seems to be a lot of the time lately."

"I've had a lot on my mind," I said, "not the least of which is what in the world I'm going to tell those kids in Round Rock about Jesus walking on the water."

Bubba took a drink of the Corona. "That's why *I'm* here - as usual," he said. "...to give you the straight scoop."

I looked at him. "You're not going to tell me you were *there*."

"No, not exactly," he said. "Let's just say I was in the general area."

"I'll take your word for it. So what do I tell these kids?"

Bubba rested his head on his hand, his elbow in the sand. "Well, let's make it easy. What would you tell anybody?"

"I'd tell them I don't know how he did it, why he did it, what it meant - and how YOU did it..." I pointed to his feet. "...without getting your boots wet."

Bubba took a long drink from the longneck. "Last part's easy, boy," he said. "I cheated."

"You cheated!?" I exclaimed. "What're you talking about?! Angels can't cheat!"

"Well, *this* one does." He looked over at me. "I sorta flapped my wings real quiet like so's you couldn't see 'em movin.' So actually I didn't exactly walk - I sorta flew."

"You're right," I said. "You cheated."

"But that's just the point, boy. It doesn't *matter* how he did it. Who *cares* how he did it?"

"Are you kidding me? *Everybody* cares how he did it."

"Maybe he knew where the rocks were!"

"BUBBA!!"

"I'm just tryin' to show ya, *they're* all missin' the point, too..."

"Which is...?"

Bubba rolled over on his back and pulled his hat down over his eyes.

"Take it from the top, boy, and I'll ask some questions and let's see if you been catchin' on to *anything* I been tellin' you all these years."

The waiter, looking at me as though I had a real problem - mumbling with absolutely no one in sight - brought nachos and two more cervezas, and Bubba and I continued.

"Okay...the story takes place after the feeding of the 5000..."

"The point of which was what...?"

"The point of which was that if you take what seems meager and insufficient and let God bless it - it will multiply beyond what is needed and be abundant."

"Good. Yore on track so far. Then what?"

"Let's see...Jesus then sends his disciples off in a boat while he dismisses the crowd."

"And what does *that* tell you?"

"Well, for one thing it tells me Jesus knew how to take charge and take care of himself. He *sent* the disciples off - *made* them get into the boat and go away - while he *dismissed* the crowd."

"That sound like a wimpy prophet to you?" Bubba uttered from under the hat.

"No."

"Then why do you suppose people portray him as so quiet and passive?"

"Beats me - they must not be reading this stuff."

"Right. In addition to the fact that they couldn't stand it if they really saw him as powerful as he is - because that would mean they are *also* that powerful - and that's just too scary for 'em." Bubba took a quick drink. "Then what does he do?"

"He goes up on a mountain to pray."

"The boy had his priorities in order, wouldn't you say?"

"Yes, I would. After all that interaction with the crowds, he probably needed some time alone, and alone with God."

"You suppose those folks you're talkin' to would get the hint from that?"

"What hint?"

"The hint that it's *im*portant to take care of *yourself*, 'cause nobody's gonna do it for you?"

"Yeah, you're right. And it's important for kids to know that too - to start early working hard and playing hard and allowing time for rest, to get centered again, like Jesus did up on the mountain in prayer."

Bubba was quiet a minute. "Wanna know what he prayed for?"

"BUBBA! That's private..."

"Not for Jesus - he prayed out loud most of the time. Made more sense to him that way."

"Well I assume he prayed for..."

"That's yore problem, boy - you always get into trouble when you go around assumin' things."

"Okay, okay. So tell me."

"He prayed for *direction*."

"What?"

"Direction. He prayed for direction." Bubba stared at me. "You know, like - which way do we go now?"

"Wait a minute." I leaned on one elbow and looked over at him. "You mean to tell me that Jesus - the Jesus in this story - didn't know what was going to happen next?"

Bubba bumped up his Stetson with the top of the longneck and rolled over to face me. "Course he didn't, boy! It all sort of unfolded as he went along. Just like your life and the lives of all the folks yore talkin' to next Sunday, kids included."

"But I thought it was all..."

"Good heaven's, son. Where DO you get yore theology from?" He disappeared under the hat again.

"Continue."

"Well, evening came and Jesus was alone on the land. He looked out and saw the disciples were having a rough time against a heavy wind."

"What time *is* it?" Bubba said.

I looked at my watch. "One p.m."

Bubba peered out from under the Stetson and rolled his eyes at me. "In the *story*, boy, in the story! WILL you pay attention?"

"Oh...sorry...uh...it says here it's the fourth watch - somewhere between 3 and 6am."

"That's right..and what do you make of that?"

I looked at the passage again. "Make of what?"

"Make of the fact that he saw them strugglin' around early night time and didn't go toward them for a few hours afterwards?"

"That is kind of strange, isn't it?"

"Not for Jesus. He let them struggle, because he trusted their strength."

"Oh, I get it...he didn't rush in to rescue them, and the more he trusted their strength, the more they trusted their own."

Bubba rolled over again and set the hat on the sand. "I do believe yore catchin' on, son!"

"I am! I am! And look at this next part! Not only doesn't he go to rescue them, but Jesus is so nonchalant about it, so unconcerned about them making it through the storm, that it says he 'meant to pass by them...' Imagine that, Bubba! Jesus just thought he'd go on and meet them on the other side of the lake - he believed they didn't need his help, he knew they could handle the storm and the boat and the waves and the lake by themselves, and so he *meant to pass them by completely* as you would somebody who you trusted to take care of the situation."

"Right, son - but look at what happened."

"Yeah. They DID see him - and they freaked out! At first they thought it was a ghost and were terrified - but then they saw it was Jesus..."

"Stop right there."

"What?"

"I said: 'Stop right there.' Whoa. Halt. You savvy?"

"Sure. Why?"

"When they thought it was a ghost and then saw it was Jesus - what does that tell ya?"

"Hmmmm - tells me that they didn't expect to see him in the midst of their trouble."

"That's right, boy. People usually don't. If they even look around in the first place they think they see everything BUT Jesus - they see ghosts, or more obstacles, or bigger problems, or easy ways out - and these folks even KNEW what the boy LOOKED like, too."

"But they didn't recognize him until he *spoke* to them, did they?"

"Nope." Bubba eyed me perilously. "And that means...?"

"That means that Jesus always makes the first move - he's with us in our journey whether in time of trouble or celebration, even when we don't know he's there or don't recognize him - and he makes the first move to let us know he's there, just like he did with the disciples in the lake."

"And what happened?"

"Again, they acted just like we do."

"Speak for yourself, boy. I ain't a human, you know."

"Yeah, sure. Anyway, the disciples did just what we do today - they were utterly astonished. They didn't believe it."

"But that shouldn't be too surprisin' - it says they didn't get the bit about the loaves either, and that message was even simpler than this one. They were a pretty dense bunch - not unlike yourselves, I might add."

"Well that really includes me I guess, 'cause I don't get this last bit about their hearts being hardened."

Bubba sat up on the beach towel and finished off the rest of the Corona.

"Boy, do I have to explain EVERYTHING to you?"

"Well, no...actually I..."

"Hand me another of them nachos and I'll see can I make you understand this."

I handed him the plate and he popped two of the gooey cheese and bean squares in his mouth, thought a minute while he chewed, then continued.

"Okay. Now see if you can get this straight....the disciples - and everyone else, I might add - got heartburn over Jesus all the time, precisely because he never did what they expected a good messiah to do. I mean, the boy was all the time tellin' them to solve their own problems, feed their own hungry, clothe their own naked, give to their own poor, heal their own sick, and, in this last story - row their own boats through their own storms."

"So they expected a messiah to rescue them, take care of them, get them out of scrapes..."

"Right - and here comes Jesus down the dusty trail tellin' them he trusts their strength more than they do!"

"But I thought he said..."

"What he said was 'It is I - have no fear.'"

"So...when they saw Jesus they totally lost faith in their own ability to make it through the storm and wanted *him* to do it for them..."

"And Jesus' reply to them, boy, what was it?"

"It was just as it was in every other story, like he said with the loaves - 'I am with you in the storm, on the journey. Most of the time you don't need me to rescue you - and even when you think you do, I won't do it. I will *come* to you, *be* with you, see you through the crisis, combining my strength *with* yours, not *instead* of yours, but WITH yours, in the boat with you, until the wind dies down and the storm ends and we are safe together on the shore once again."

"That's right, boy. And that's why this story is *not* about Jesus walking on the water. Which, by the way, is where that horrible joke came from."

"What joke, Bubba?"

"The one about 'Why did Jesus cross the lake?'"

"What?"

"To get to the other side..."

"BUBBA! That is terrible! But you're right that this story isn't about walking on water. It ought to be called The Story of The Astonished Disciples! Jesus is just doing what he always did - and the disciples *still* aren't getting it, catching on, clicking to his message."

"Not bad, son," Bubba smiled. "I do believe you're gettin' it."

I frowned.

"Good grief, boy! Now what's the matter? We just wrote your whole sermon together."

"I still have a problem. What am I gonna tell the kids?"

"Tell them the truth."

"Oh no. Not that."

"Yep. They gotta hear it sooner or later."

"Uh...*which* truth."

"The one in the story."

"Oh - the one about how Jesus trusts them, trusts their strength, trusts their courage, trusts their love; the one about how he's with them in the midst of their storms - trusting them - and encouraging them with his strength as well, combining his with theirs to overcome all the storms of their lives."

"Yep - that truth."

"And do you think their parents will listen to it too?"

"I don't know. Be interestin' if they treated their kids, and each other, that way. I'm not real optimistic. You humans' hearts sure get hardened when Jesus isn't the way you want him to be. Give it a shot, though. Who knows what will happen?"

Bubba sat up and pulled his bulky frame to a standing position.

"Well, now that I got that done, I gotta be on my way, boy. Other fish to fry, if you know what I mean."

"Where are you going now?"

He pointed up in the sky at a man in a parachute being towed by a motorboat.

"I'm gonna go up there and scare the fool out of that boy in the parasail. Just sort of mosey up there beside him and say 'Howdy, partner. Havin' a nice day?'"

"Bubba! You can't *do* that!"

"Oh, you just don't let me have any fun, boy." He smiled and pointed to the seashore. "Why don't you just walk me out there and I'll be on my way."

"Sure, Bubba," I said, standing and walking beside him. "And thanks for the help with the sermon. It was enlightening, as usual."

"Just give credit where credit's due, son. And tell 'em the truth."

"You got it, Bubba," I said as I watched him wade out into the water - and then do his walking stunt again. "Take care of yourself."

"Yeah. You too," he said, with a grin on his face. "And good luck thinkin' up somethin' to tell all those people behind you who saw you walkin' out here to the water with me..."

I turned around to see an awe-struck crowd with eyes and mouths wide open gawking at the figure walking across the top of the waves. As the huge angel flew up and out of sight, their eyes turned slowly to me.

"Bubba!" I yelled. "Get me out of this!"

"Remember what the story's about, boy! Jesus doesn't rescue you - just says he'll be with you through the storm. And this ain't even a piddlin' shower compared to the clouds ahead."

I heard him laugh in the distance.

"You'll do just fine, boy. Trust your strength. You - and everybody else - will do just fine."

I turned toward the shouting, smiling, crying crowd and hoped that sainthood would not be too painful.

Mark 6.7-13

And he called to him the twelve and began to send them out two by two, and gave them authority over the unclean spirits. He charged them to take nothing for their journey except a staff; no bread, no bag, no money in their belts; but to wear sandals and not put on two tunics. And he said to them, "Where you enter a house, stay there until you leave the place. And if any place will not receive you and they refuse to hear you, when you leave, shake off the dust that is on your feet for a testimony against them."

So they went out and preached that men should repent. And they cast out many demons, and anointed with oil many that were sick and healed them.

Bubba Dust

I was jogging down Town Lake trail last week sweating my brains out and wondering what to say about the Gospel for today, when I suddenly heard something approaching from behind. It sounded like a rhinoceros with emphysema. I turned to see a familiar 250 pound angel in a UT orange sweat suit looking like a giant popsicle melting in the relentless Austin sun.

"Bubba!" I yelled, as I slowed my pace. "What are *you* doing here?"

"Don't...slow...up...for me, boy," he said, trying to maintain his pace. "Got...to...lose some weight...and soon."

"Then slow down, Bubba," I said. "You'll kill yourself in this heat."

"Cain't...kill...myself, son....I'm...already...a angel...remember?"

"Well, slow down and walk a few minutes," I argued. "Catch your breath, like the song says."

"What...song...is that?"

"You know...'He walks with me and he talks with me...'"

"Okay...okay," he said, slowing down and walking beside me, dripping wet from sweat. "I guess I could use a little 'joy we share as we tarry there.' And speakin' o' which - got any joy juice to re-plenish some o' this holy water?"

"I've got some in a cooler in the back of my car. We can walk to it. But I thought you were trying to lose weight?"

"I am, son, I am. The Boss's on that 'body is the temple of the spirit' thing again and all the heavenly host are workin' real hard to get in shape. Of course, *I'm* leadin' the pack."

"You have more to lead with," I mumbled.

"What's that, boy?"

"I said you're a good leader, Bubba. Now tell me what you're doing on this trail specifically. You never go anywhere without a reason."

"I thought you might want some company to run with, son. Your thoughts about that Gospel lesson sounded like you needed some help."

"You *heard* my thoughts?"

"Well, something like that. It's too hard to explain to you right now."

As we walked we were passed by two attractive women in jogging outfits who smiled and waved.

"You don't have to be no psychic telepath to read *yore* mind, ya know."

"Bubba!! Stop that!! Besides, I was thinking about the Gospel when..."

"Yeah, sure, me too, boy. Now where's that automobile of yores with the special enzyme replenisher in the trunk."

"You mean the beer?"

"Hush, boy. I gotta tell the Boss what I had today and it's right hard to lie to That One.

"Just around the next corner. So tell me about the Gospel."

"What do you wanta know?"

"Everything. How come Jesus sent them out 'two by two?' Why didn't he send them out one by one or in groups of three so they'd get a fourth for bridge or something?"

"Boy, just think of where they were going and what they were gonna do there! I mean, these fellas were headin' into some rough territory, with people who didn't take kindly to some new magician comin' into town and messin' with their trade, if you get my drift."

"If I get any more of your drift, I'll pass out. Why don't you stand under that shower a minute and rinse off?"

"That's yore trouble, boy, yore too involved with the body and not enough with the spirit." He got under the outdoor shower and I held it for him while he got soaked, continuing to splurt through the spray. "Pfffft, pfffft, and that was another reason they went two at a time. Jesus figgered they'd look after each other better that way. Sorta help keep each other on the road."

"Okay, okay. The sun will dry you off in no time now. Come over here to the car." We walked to the trunk of the Honda and soon were sitting on a bench with two cold Shiner Bock longnecks in our hands. "So what was the deal about giving them authority over the unclean spirits? How'd he do that?"

"Simple, son. He just told them they already had it."

"Had what?"

"Authority over unclean spirits."

"They already *had* it? Is that because they were special?"

"Good heavens, no, son! They were just a bunch of good ol' boys just like that congregation at church. They had it in 'em all the time. Just took Jesus to tell 'em so they'd notice it and use it."

"But what exactly does that mean, that 'authority over unclean spirits'?"

"Means what it says, boy. It means that every-body has the ability to see the unclean spirits in them-selves *and* in other people. It means y'all can tell in a Houston minute whether a person is filled with fear, envy, jealousy, power hunger, lust, and greed. And you know whether those little demons are in your-self also, starin' right back at you in yore mirror."

"Yeah, I suppose you're right."

"Ain't no 'supposin'' about it, boy. You *know* I'm right. The thing is that most people don't believe they can help anyone else get rid of those demons - because they might have to give up some of their own in the process. You humans *do* love to hang onto those little devils. You think y'all cain't get along without them, or so it seems."

"So the disciples went around with the ability to do what they called back then 'casting out demons' because they were willing to give up some of their own?"

"Now ya got it, son. You know, it takes a while to get through to you but once you catch on you ain't half bad." He dumped his empty bottle into the trash can. "Got another longneck? I need to tell you about that next question on your mind."

"And that is...?"

"You're gonna ask me: 'What is healing?'"

"I'll get you the beer. Don't move." I brought him another cold Shiner Bock and one for myself as well. "Okay, how'd you know that?"

"Ya learn it in angel school, son. But let me get on with the story."

"Please do."

"Well, what they meant by healing is a far cry from what y'all do down at the hospital fixin' bones, and givin' drugs, and shootin' pictures inside of folks and like that. The disciples didn't have none of that stuff to work with anyway, ya know."

"No kidding?"

"Yeah, and so healing meant a lot more than fixin' bodies."

"But to hear clergy and doctors talk the only thing that counts is some physical change - that's what healing means, some change in the body."

"It's a lot broader than that, boy. All kinds of things can be healed: memories can be healed, dreams can be healed, relationships can be healed, self images and angers and resentments of a lifetime and guilts and hurts all can be healed. All those demons can be cast out with the help of others, including your own."

"But what about bodies?"

"Sometimes bodies are also fixed in the process, but that's not the main point, boy! The main point is all that other stuff needs takin' care of and CAN be too, if people want it to be and let it be."

"Do I have to ask the next question or do you just want to tell me?"

Bubba looked at me intently. "Let's see, uh, I think you already know the answer to why Jesus sent them out without any money or food or suitcase."

"Yeah, that's pretty easy. Possessions get in the way of healing, right?"

"You got it, boy. It's right hard to be interested in other people and even to get a good look at yourself if you got to be worried about car payments and Visa bills and a mortgage company lookin' for the next check."

"Yes, but...

"Now just keep yore spurs on, son, nobody's suggestin' you tell everybody to go liquidate their house and put on rags and hitchhike up IH 35 to Dallas, though the Boss knows Dallas could use a herd o' people like that. No, what Jesus was pointin' to and what I'm sayin' is that you got to get yore priorities in order - and you'll never be a healer, of yourself or anyone else if those possessions are first priority."

"I see."

"I know ya do. And speakin' of possessions, I think I'd like to possess one more longneck before I tackle the rest of the runnin' trail."

"You don't 'possess' beer, Bubba, you just rent it," I said, getting him another one.

"Well I'll rent me this one while you ask me about the house."

"Why bother?"

"Ask me anyway. I don't always get it with you."

"You don't?"

"Nope, you got so many things goin' through yore mind at one time it's hard to pick which one is comin' up first. Sorta like lookin' at a barrel full o' frogs."

"Thanks alot. The first frog up wants to know what Jesus meant about staying in the house until you leave the place?"

"Meant what he said, boy. And what he said was, 'keep yore mind on yore bidness and only do one thing at a time.' Don't go around tryin' to heal everything in sight. Just concentrate on what yore doin' and take it slow' - unlike those frogs in yore brain I might add."

"Isn't it about time for you to be sloshing down the jogging trail?"

"Why do I get the feelin' that you aren't gonna use any of that great information I gave you for yore story?"

"I'm not sure I buy it. I think I'll write about Amos."

"Great choice, boy. It's the same thing. The Boss told Amos he already had the authority in him, just needed a direction was all, a little somethin' to do. And whatever you write, make sure you tell 'em about the re-wards of all this prophecyin' and healin' and the like."

"Do I have to?"

"Yep, to be fair, you have to. If they want to get rid of other people's demons and to get rid of their own and be healers and prophets, or even normal, run of the mill Christians for that matter, they better know what they're gettin' into beforehand."

"But if I tell them the demons include getting involved in political campaigns and divesting South African stocks and working for justice and ending hunger - what'll they say?"

"Don't know, boy, you never know till you ask. And remember, those are just the demons that possess everybody and prevent y'all from healing each other. To ask others to give up their demons you have to be willing to give up your own, and that includes yore prejudices, yore social status, and yore possessions."

"That's a radical Gospel, Bubba."

"Yep, Jesus was no pansy, boy. And I'm not either. I gotta run, so to speak."

Before I knew it, Bubba had vanished into thin air, or in his case, thick air, leaving a small, pyramid-like pile of rubble in front of the bench.

"What's that?" I asked to no one in particular.

"That there's Bubba dust, boy. Pass it out next time you're in church. Tell 'em if they run into people who don't want to listen to the message, or accept the healin' Jesus offers 'em, or admit that they've already got authority over unclean spirits, shake some of that stuff off yore Reebok's at 'em. Then tell 'em to get the heck out of there. Some folks they'll be talkin' to got no sense of humour at all."

"Oh, everybody's got a sense of humour, Bubba."

"I hope you're right for yore sake, boy."

"What do you mean?"

"I mean I hope that park police guy standin' behind you's got one. He's wonderin' what you're doin' standin' there with a beer bottle in yore hand and shoutin' up in the air to somebody nobody can hear but you."

"Thanks a lot, Bubba."

"Any time, son. Happy trails."

I turned to see the officer walking up to me with a strange look in his eye. I suddenly realized I was getting more and more like Bubba.

With just one look I could read the officer's mind.

Luke 7.1-10

After he had ended all his sayings in the hearing of the people he entered Capernaum. Now a centurion had a slave who was dear to him, who was sick and at the point of death. When he heard of Jesus, he sent to him elders of the Jews, asking him to come and heal his slave. And when they came to Jesus, they besought him earnestly, saying, "He is worthy to have you do this for him, for he loves our nation, and he built us our synagogue." And Jesus went with them.

When he was not far from the house, the centurion sent friends to him, saying to him, "Lord, do not trouble yourself, for I am not worthy to have you come under my roof; therefore I did not presume to come to you. But say the word, and let my servant be healed. For I am a man set under authority, with soldiers under me: and I say to one, 'Go,' and he goes; and to another, 'Come,' and he comes; and to my slave, 'Do this,' and he does it." When Jesus heard this he marveled at him, and turned and said to the multitude that followed him, "I tell you, not even in Israel have I found such faith." And when those who had been sent returned to the house, they found the slave well.

Bubba and Sylvia

I t was a dark and stormy night. Actually, it had been raining for hours as I sat in the house alone at my desk pouring over the Gospel for Sunday and glancing through two or three Biblical commentaries. The passage seemed stranger than usual and there were a couple of things I hoped I could figure out before I started to write this story. Just as I was feeling totally bewildered, a booming voice from behind jump-started me out of the chair.

"It ain't *in* the *books*, son." I whirled around to see the familiar, and slightly overweight face of my old friend.

"Bubba! What're *you* doing here?"

"You know, you always ask me that, son. Just once I'd like to hear you say somethin' like 'Hi. I'm glad to see ya.' Or 'Hot dang, I thought you'd never get here.'"

"Okay," I said. "Hi-I'm-glad-to-see-you."

"Better. Not great, but better."

"Good," I said. "Now, what in the world *are* you doing here?"

"Are you comatose, boy? Don't you know it's *stormin'* out there?"

I looked at him carefully. "But you aren't even wet."

"'Course not. Angels don't *get* wet. At least *this* angel don't. Why, it can be rainin' up a frog stranglin' gully washer and I get around dry as an ant hill in August." He nervously looked outside. "Hate water. Reminds me of that flood thing the Boss did back in Genesis. I never *have* gotten over that."

"So how do you...?"

"No," he continued as if I hadn't spoken, "...it ain't the rain - it's really the lightnin'."

"You don't get wet but you can get hit with lightning?"

"That's right. Ever since that Lucifer incident The Boss wants to keep His options open - if ya know what I mean..."

"Sure but..."

"So, since I was playin' duck and dodge with the lightnin' bolts and happened to be in the area, I thought I'd drop in and see how the story was goin'."

"Not so good," I said. "This is a weird passage."

"Careful what you call the Gospel, boy. *You* ain't exactly immune to lightnin' bolts either."

"But it *is* weird. I mean the whole thing takes place *in absentia*."

"That *is* strange," Bubba said. "I thought it was in Capernaum."

I glared at him. "You're a *big* help.

"Sorry, son. But you make a great straight man."

"Well can you compose yourself enough to listen to me a minute?"

"Sure, boy. You go right ahead," he said, pulling up the most comfortable chair in the room. "I'll just make myself to home."

"Great," I replied intently. "Let me take it from the beginning. First of all we don't know anything about the slave - no name, no disease, we don't even know if it was a man or a woman."

"It was a woman named Sylvia. She had a virus."

"How do you know that?" I looked at the smirk on his face. "Oh, no. Don't tell me *you* were there?

"Well, now that you asked, yes, actually, I was. Seems it had been rainin' and lightnin' a lot like to-night and I stopped off to take shelter in Capernaum. Course the folks there were a mite better in the host department."

"You keep talking - I'll get the Shiner," I said, leaving the room for the kitchen. Bubba continued in a loud voice.

"Yes. I remember Sylvia well. She was a devoted servant. I mean, she had been with that family for years. In fact, as you know, Roman law says she was considered family, even with some inheritance rights."

"So why didn't Luke mention that in his Gospel?" I said, returning with a cold six pack. "It would have made the story more interesting."

"Luke wasn't tryin' to be Louis Lamour, boy. He had a point to tell and didn't care much about yore readin' enjoyment."

"Okay, so she had a virus. And the centurion - would you care to tell me *his* name too?"

"Not important, boy. I shouldn't have told you Sylvia's name. Before you know it, you'll be wantin' the name of their dog and cat."

"They had a dog and cat?"

"What're you doin' here, son, readin' the Gospel or takin' a census?"

"Okay, okay. So Sylvia was sick and her devoted master, the centurion, is concerned about her."

"More than concerned, boy! He was devastated. She was like a second mother to him."

"What happened to his first mother?"

"There you go again."

"Oh. Sorry. So why did he go to the elders of the synagogue? Why didn't he go directly to Jesus?"

Bubba took a long drink from the longneck. "Simple, boy. He was a military man - so he went through channels, chain of command, as he thought he should." Bubba leaned forward in the chair. "The Boss has got channels too, but they're backwards from the way y'all work. It's the first last and the last first and like that."

"Wonderful. But I still don't get why the centurion didn't want to talk directly to Jesus. Jesus never lays eyes on either one of them - either the centurion *or* the slave. The centurion first sends the elders and then sends his friends to deliver the message."

"Maybe he was *embarrassed*," Bubba said. "He *was* a pagan you know, and not supposed to be believing in Jesus' works. Maybe he was worried someone might report him to his superiors."

"Possibly. Or maybe he was genuinely ashamed and humble, feeling unworthy and grateful for any help Jesus could give his servant."

"As I recall seein' him, it was a little bit of both. He really was at his wit's end. The physicians had written her off for as good as dead, so the centurion decided he'd try one last thing. He'd heard about this Jesus fella from the rumors in the barracks - and thought he'd ask him if he could heal her."

"But that's just it, Bubba. Not once does Jesus say she's healed. He doesn't even see her or touch her."

"Depends on who you talk to."

"What's that supposed to mean?"

"Means just what I said, boy. Depends on whether you believe Matthew or Luke. Matthew has Jesus sayin' 'Be it done as you have believed.'"

"Now you're going to tell me that I have to believe one of the Gospels over the other ones?"

"Didn't say nothin' of the kind, boy. Just want you to remember that's there always more than two sides to the story."

"But still... that seems to put it back on the centurion's faith and not on the faith of Sylvia."

"Now you're startin' to get the point, boy. I thought you'd never catch on. It was just like those folks lowerin' that guy down through the roof tiles..." Bubba looked at me. "You *do* remember that one, don't you?"

"Sure, but what...?"

"And it says 'When Jesus saw *their* faith, he was healed.' So healing has nothing to do with the faith of the sick person - it's the faith of the folks *around* that person that makes healing happen."

"Now I'm getting really confused, Bubba. Hand me a cold one and run this by me again - on slow speed. How exactly did this Sylvia get well?"

"I don't like the phrase 'get well,' boy. Sounds too much like those faith healers y'all tolerate down here. I like the word 'healed' a lot better."

"Why?"

"Because y'all humans think healing means getting totally restored to health, when it don't mean nothin' of the kind."

"But...but..."

"Ya sound like a motorboat, son. Let it out!"

"But I thought healing was..."

"Right. But it's not. Healin' means lettin' the Boss into the situation - and giving up the outcome. Think about it! That outcome depends on how messed up the person's body is." He sat back in his chair. "Don't never confuse healin' with gettin' well."

"Okay, okay. So did Sylvia get healed?"

"You tell me. You went to seminary and studied this stuff."

"Yeah, but you were *there.*"

"That's just the point, boy. It don't make no difference if you were there in person or there readin' about it in Luke 2000 years later. The truth is the truth no matter what happened. So, you tell me." He crossed his ankles, and pursed his lips to listen.

"Okay," I said. "I will."

"Go for it."

"I think the three things that healed her were love, humility and faith. And in that particular order, too."

"Well, two out of three ain't bad. Go ahead and tell me about love and humility."

"The family loved Sylvia so much they were willing to ask the centurion, perhaps at some risk to his career and to his family's standing in the community, to see if Jesus would consent to visit them. I think that's what attracted Jesus in the first place. He was amazed that someone with so much worldly authority and power and popularity as that soldier had would risk it - not for belief in Jesus - but for the love of this servant. It was the *love* Jesus responded to and the *risk* they took to show it."

"Not bad, son, even for you. Now what about the humility?"

"It takes *humility* to *risk* love, to risk being

vulnerable against all odds, to lay down our own sense of power and to put ourselves totally into the hands of another."

"Now you're gettin' it, son. And that's what Jesus saw as 'faith,'" Bubba said. "It wasn't faith in Jesus so much as it was the centurion's love for the servant that Jesus commented on when he said 'I sure haven't seen this, even in Israel.'"

"And that's another point too, Bubba."

"What's that?"

"That the supposedly believing community is shown up by the pagan unbelievers once again. And that's really no different from today. It's the secular groups that are in the forefront of raising environmental concerns, lobbying for healthcare and other social reforms, and searching for peaceful solutions to world conflict. The church is constantly being confronted with its own smugness, laziness, or its assumption that spiritual matters have nothing to do with secular ones. That centurion is represented today by lots of people *outside* the church."

"That's right boy. But there's one more point I need to tell ya that ol' Luke didn't tell in the story."

"What's that, Bubba?"

The big angel leaned forward in his chair.

"Sylvia died."

"Sylvia died?"

"Well, of *course* she died, boy. You don't see her down at the K-Mart Blue Light Special do ya?"

"But I thought she was healed?"

"She was."

"But then...."

"I see. So even if she got well, or better..."

"Or *whatever*..."

"Right...or whatever for a while - she, like the rest of us - would eventually die."

"That's right, son. Welcome to Earth - the death rate here is 100%. One out of one dies. But that don't mean healing don't happen along the way."

"Or that healing and death might be the same thing? That often death is in fact a form of healing?"

"Right again, boy. The healing that took place around Sylvia's illness was phenomenal. People rallied, relationships were made more valuable, the church was challenged, Jesus himself was amazed, love was again made manifest - and all of that is healing, son - even in the process of Sylvia's dyin'."

Bubba looked out the window as he finished the Shiner.

"And speaking of dyin' - that lightnin' is dyin' down some so I can be on my way again." He stood from the chair and stretched out his magnificent wings. "Thanks for the re-freshment and the talk. I always like hearin' you talk, boy. You always come around to my way of thinkin,' even if you are stubborn about it. "

"Well, thanks for the information about Sylvia, Bubba. I'll pass it along to the folks at church on

Sunday."

"Just make sure you give credit where credit's due, boy."

"No problem, Bubba," I said as he walked out the front door and lifted off into the night. "Oh, wait a second," I hollered, "...I do have one last question."

"Make it quick, boy! What is it?"

"What happened to the centurion's first mother?"

Bubba yelled back over his shoulder. "She got a job on Dallas playin' Miss Ellie."

Just then a huge lightning bolt flashed within inches of Bubba's ascending body. As the thunder rumbled across the sky, I barely heard Bubba's plaintive voice saying:

"Just *jokin'* with him...I was just *jokin'* with him....."

Luke 2.15-21

When the angels went away from them into heaven, the shepherds said to one another, "Let us go over to Bethlehem and see this thing that has happened, which the Lord has made known to us." And they went with haste, and found Mary and Joseph, and the babe lying in a manger. And when they saw it they made known the saying which had been told them concerning this child; and all who heard it wondered at what the shepherds told them. But Mary kept all these things, pondering them in her heart. And the shepherds returned, glorifying God and praising God for all they had heard and seen, as it had been told them.

And at the end of eight days, when he was circumcised, he was called Jesus, the name given by the angel before he was conceived in the womb.

Bubba and God

This story is about a baby named Jesus. It is a true story and all the events are accurate and factual, because I got all the information directly from Bubba the Texas Angel who was, in fact, actually there. Or so he told me.

One day a long, long, time ago, God strolled across heaven, enjoying the bright sunshine and the fluffy clouds, and smiling and nodding politely at all the other spirits up there who just liked to be around him and listen to him hum or whistle or sometimes even sing. God was in a particularly good mood that morning because he had gotten up early and jogged while the sun rose and then had a great breakfast and a shower and felt really pleased with the way things were going in the universe. He was whistling a tune he had heard in the Peruvian rainforest, and trying to match it with something from Mozart, and the result was really quite nice, when one of the angels who had been gone for a couple of days came flapping furiously up to God, sweating and smelling like Luling oilfields in August.

"You've got to *do* something, Boss!" the angel exclaimed.

God stopped in his tracks and looked at the angel like he was out of his eternal mind. "At the risk of stating the obvious," God said, "I already *have* done something." He pointed to the earth. "We are talking pigs, chickens, cows, birds, plants, and even people, here. Or isn't *that* enough?"

"But that's the problem..."

"The *problem*?" God said, his wide eyes looking puzzled. "There is a *problem*?" His huge voice rolled like thunder across the heavens.

The angel suddenly realized that maybe he had just stepped into something that was going to be hard to get off of his cowboy boots. (Of course the angel in question here was Bubba.) But he persisted anyway because it was very important. "Well," Bubba said, "..as a matter of fact, God...yes there *is* a problem."

"Great..." God continued, sitting down on a large grey cloud with his elbows on his knees and his head in his hands to think a minute. "What did I forget this time? Or are they still complaining about mosquitos and flies? So I messed up a little..."

"It's not the mosquitos or the flies...and I don't think it's something you forgot."

"Well, *that's* a relief. What *is* it then?"

Bubba cleared a hole in the clouds in front of God.

"Actually, it's something *they* forgot." He pointed down to the earth. "Look..."

So God looked down and this is what he saw:

- air polluted by carelessness
- water dirty and undrinkable
- people aiming weapons at each other and destroying cities
- people dying of strange diseases
- some people with lots of money and many with none
- some people with too much to eat and others starving
- many people unhappy and sad and feeling lost or alone.

And for a brief moment, God could not speak. He just watched and watched. When he sat back down, Bubba noticed that a few trickles of tears were coming out of God's eyes, so the angel tore off a piece of cloud and handed it to God to blow his nose. And he did. (It sounded like a rhinoceros, but Bubba was too polite to say so.)

"What happened?" God asked, nearly in a whisper.

"They, uh...they forgot."

"Again?"

"Yes, God. Again." Bubba sat down beside God, handed him another piece of cloud and winced while the rhinoceros sound bellowed through the air.

All the other spirits and angels and archangels and cherubim and seraphim had vanished, waiting to see what God would do. Only Bubba sat there with God, until there appeared out of a distant cloud a little pussycat face, and then a furry body, and then a long pussycat tail. The cat slowly walked up to God and rubbed up against his leg, then against his other leg, then, with a quick leap, jumped into God's lap and purred while it waited to be petted. Absently, God's delicate hand gently stroked the cat while he talked with the angel.

"How could they forget?"

"They're human, remember? You made them that way."

"Yes, but I thought they would remember the most basic thing about our relationship...that I *love* them and, because of that they can love one another, and the land, and the air and the sea and the animals and all that I gave them to take care of and use for eternity."

Bubba thought for a minute. He knew he was on shaky clouds here, explaining to God about creation, but he was a Texan and Texans take chances, so he went for it.

"They have short memories, God, humans do. And a lot of other stuff gets in the way, kind of takes over their attention, distracts them from what you had in mind..."

"But," God shook his bushy head and squinted up his eyes, "...what can I do to remind them of what our purpose is, of who they are, of who I am, of what the universe is about?"

Bubba crossed his legs, which made his spurs jangle, and rested his Stetson on his knee. The cat jumped from God's great lap and batted at the spinning star in Bubba's spurs. The angel tried to ignore the animal - which he equated with kids and dogs - and looked back at God.

"So are you yankin' my reins or what?" Bubba asked.

"Come again?"

"How come *you're* askin' *me* what to do about this? *You're* God, remember?"

God smiled and showed his one gold tooth in his ancient wide mouth and said, "If I had all this figured out, I wouldn't ask you. Sometimes I need a little help from you..." He pointed down through the hole in the cloud. "...and also from them. You *do* understand the word 'partners' don't you?"

"In Texas we say 'pardners,' but, yeah, I get it. You want some help? I'm your man - I mean angel."

"Okay. What do we do?" asked God.

"Send a prophet."

"Done that," God said.

"Send some locusts, or a hurricane, or fahr aints..."

"You mean fire ants..."

"That's what I said, fahr aints, or killer bees..."

"Done that."

"How about a pharaoh, or a dictator, or a hero or two?"

"Done that."

Bubba scratched his head, then looked at the cat.

"Nobody would believe it," God said.

"Believe what?"

"If I sent the cat."

"How'd you know what I was thinking?"

God smiled again. "There are still *some* things I can do."

Bubba finally said in desperation. "Then good grief, God, why don't you just go yourself?"

"Are you kidding?" God pulled a thick black book out of a pocket in his saffron robe. "Have you seen my *schedule* for the next million years?"

"Cancel it." Bubba picked up the cat and handed it back to God. "Cancel all of it. This event is more important."

God thought a minute (which in God's timeframe could have been a century or two) and stroked the purring pussycat. Then he looked back at Bubba. "Good idea. I'll do it. I'll just go down there and appear in front of them all and tell them how much I love them and..."

"Nope. Cain't do that," Bubba said, before he knew what was coming out of his mouth. "Uh...what I meant was..."

"Go ahead. See if you can get the other boot in there and tell me *why* I can't do that?" The cat licked his hand. "I'm *God*, and I can do anything I want to.....can't I?"

"Not exactly," Bubba said cautiously. "Ya see, it's exactly because you *are* God that you'll scare the bejeebers out of 'em. They'll take one good look at you and it'll do 'em in, they won't be able to stand it."

"Stand *what*? I stood under a rain cloud after I jogged and I don't smell any worse than *you* do."

"It's not that," Bubba said. "It's....your *face*."

God looked at Bubba, not certain how to respond. Then he said: "Now wait just a minute here...what's the *matter* with my face?" He looked at his lap where the sleeping feline was purring. "Doesn't bother the cat."

Bubba rolled his eyes and shook his head. "It's all that *light*, God. Oh sure, we're used to you - but even I have to put on sunglasses sometimes when you get excited about something." He pointed to the hole in the cloud. "And these are human beings. You'd just be too overwhelming for them. They'd be so scared that they wouldn't understand you."

"Then I'll go incognito, in disguise, with dark glasses and a hat and maybe a big moustache and an umbrella and..."

"Not fair. You got to go as yourself, but in a way that they can sort of get to know you, kind of ease on up to you and listen to what you have to say. Like sittin' on the tailgate, sippin' on longnecks."

"Well, how in the world will I ever..?" Suddenly God stood up and the dozing cat fell off his lap right through the cloud and had to crawl back up top using his claws. "I've got it!" God said. "I'll go as a.....BABY!"

"No offense, God," Bubba began, "...but that is one of the worst, most ridiculous ideas you have ever..."

"NO! It's GREAT! It's a *great* idea!" And God danced around with his hands in the air to music only he could hear, and the cat hid behind Bubba with its eyes staring wide. "Why didn't I think of that before?"

Bubba frowned. "I think you'd be better off as a cat. If you think they're mad about the mosquitoes and flies, wait till the reviews come in on *this* one..."

"And we'll have great pageantry, and a wonderful, passionate story, and a great star in the heavens, and shepherds, and three wise men - no, make that *four* - and animals - some sheep and donkeys and elephants, I love elephants..."

"'Elephants'?" Bubba knew they would have to be deleted.

"...And maybe a barn or something to be born in, and DRAMA, we must have DRAMA, so maybe a small hotel with an innkeeper who..."

"Don't forget angels," Bubba added, almost sarcastically.

"YES!!! ANGELS!!! LOTS of angels!!" God was nearly beside himself with joy at the possibilities. He looked down through the hole in the cloud and pointed. "They'll LOVE it! And they'll *finally* get the message that I love them and they can love one another and take care of each other and the earth."

Bubba pursed his lips. He wondered if he should say what he was thinking.

"How could they do that?" God asked, reading Bubba's mind again. "How could they reject him, this tiny little baby that wouldn't hurt a flea?"

Bubba pointed down again. "They did all *that*, and they keep forgetting. Maybe they don't *want* to hear that you love them."

"It doesn't matter," God said firmly. "We'll keep telling them till they *do* remember. And we'll make this baby story so wonder-full that they'll want to hear it and celebrate it *every year!*"

Bubba shook his head. "I hate to be the practical one around here...but how are you gonna *do* this baby thing?"

God's eyes flashed like a shooting star. "With gusto, with flair, with pageantry - there must be all the important things in the story, like sharing, and giving, and sacrifice, and risk and adventure and, most important of all, love."

"That's not what I meant, God and you *know* it."

"I was avoiding the answer."

"Right - so how you gonna *do* it?"

God motioned Bubba over to the hole in the cloud. They both knelt down and peered over the edge. The pussycat did too and nearly fell over.

"Uuuuuuuhhhhhhh...." God said, looking down to the earth. "I choose *that* one."

Bubba and the cat squinted their eyes. "*Which* one?"

God pointed way, way down to a young couple who were just about to get married.

"She's going to have a baby boy in nine months and it's going to be me - sort of. I mean it will be him *and* me. And our name will be.......uh...let's see, what would I like to be called...hmmmmmm..." God's smile broadened and the sun gleamed off his gold tooth. "I think I'll be called...JESUS...because in my language that means 'He loves his people.'"

Bubba groaned and sat back down. "Oh no."

"Oh no *what*?" God asked, as puzzled as usual that anyone could have questions about something which seemed perfectly clear and reasonable to him.

"Do you know how they're gonna try to *explain* all of this?"

God grinned and the wrinkles puckered in his ruddy dark face. "It'll give them fits, I'll bet," he snickered. "But who cares? It doesn't *matter* how they explain it. And it doesn't even matter how I did it. What matters is *that* I did it. I came to them, can-celled my calendar for them, spent time with them and learned from them because I love them and want them to know it, and want them to tell each other the story again and again and again."

"Well," Bubba said, "...*this* should certainly *do* it."

"Great," God said, standing up and stretching. "So get started. You've got a lot to do..."

"ME?" Bubba frowned. "*I've* got a lot to do?"

"Yes, you. I have to go change into Holy Spirit. You go round up some shepherds, and get the star ready, and...oh yes...put some angels on call for the blessed event...scare up some wise men - make one of them a woman, will you?...and it would be nice if there were some music, but I'll understand if Mozart is busy, and reserve the stable in Bethlehem...that nice couple down there's going to need it in a few months - I think it's Mary and Joseph, isn't it?...and get somebody to write all this down in a Bible or something so they'll read the story year after year and remember..." God's voice trailed off as he happily danced through the clouds. "Oh....this will be *so* much fun..."

Bubba hurriedly wrote down a list of all the things God wanted him to do and then flew off all over heaven and earth making the arrangements. Well, the rest, as they say, is history, and we hear about it every year at Christmas, just like God wanted:

"And it came to pass that an angel appeared to Joseph in a dream saying: 'Y'all will have a baby and call him *Jesus*.' And Mary gave birth to Jesus in a stable because there was no room in the inn. And an angel announced the birth to shepherds in their fields who immediately went to the stable to see the baby.

And wise men followed a great star which hung over the stable in Bethlehem."

And God was in that Jesus baby, and slowly got to know us human beings and we got to know him. And Jesus grew up and did things to constantly tell everyone how much God loves them and forgives them and wants the best for them and will be with them in times of change and stability, and gain and loss, and death and life, and pain and happiness. He is there clapping and cheering when we do something successful or fun, and listening when we're feeling angry, and crying with us when we're feeling sad because someone died.

And just in case we ever forget all that, God has arranged to retell the story of Jesus' birth so we hear it and celebrate it every year at Christmas, for the rest of our lives together. Because when God was born into the world in Jesus an amazing thing happened. At that very same time, God was born into the world through each of us - and is still within us laughing and crying and dancing and running and talking and hoping that we will remember how much he loves us so we can love one another and take care of this earth he gave us, until we meet again.

References

Books by Chuck Meyer

Surviving Death: A Practical Guide to Caring for the Dying and Bereaved. 23rd Publications, Mystic, Connecticut, 1988, Second Edition, 1991. ($9.95) - This book is for those who care for the dying, the families and friends of the terminally ill, those who have experienced the death of a close loved one, and those who themselves are dying. Dr. Karl Slaikeu, author of Up From The Ashes says: "...the book is unsurpassed in its concrete, step-by-step instructions on everything from walking into the patient's room, to talking with dying and bereaved individuals and coping with the full range of emotions and behavioral demands that survivors face. The author's blend of humor and sensitivity is especially refreshing." Winner of the Violet Crown Award for best non-fiction book of 1991, Austin Writer's League. (175pp.)

God's Laughter and Other Heresies. Stone Angel Books, Austin, Texas, Second Edition 1992. ($9.95). The author guarantees that "the buying of this book will definitely increase your own personal chances of getting into heaven." If heaven is a place of joy, sadness, tears and laughter, then he is correct, for the book is filled with all of the above. In addition to the slightly irreverent commentaries on "Babies," "Stress," and "Bible Misquotes," the Christmas stories of "A Donkey Named Glory," "The Fourth Wise Man," "Harold the Innkeeper," and "An Angel Named Bubba," make delightful reading to children. (238pp.)

The Eighth Day, Letters, Poems and Parables. Stone Angel Books, Austin, Texas 1991. ($8.95). The Eighth Day is the day after God finished making everything and rested. It is the time *after* the seventh day and *before* Jesus comes back. It is sort of a Christian Twilight Zone where the Holy Spirit plays Rod Serling. These "letters, poems and parables" retell Bible stories from the viewpoint of the characters themselves. The Widow's Story, The Lawyer's Confession, Three Days in Saul's Head, Leper Letter, and The Paralytic's Point of View, vividly portray the feelings and thoughts of ordinary people encountering an ordinary Jesus with extraordinary results for the rest of their lives. (175pp.)

The Gospel According to Bubba. Stone Angel Books, Austin, Texas, 1992. ($9.95). A 250lb Texas angel named Bubba appeared at the author's front door with "inside" information from "The Boss" and one heck of a thirst. It was down hill from there. Bubba's (unsolicited) insights are as Lone Star as "fahr aints." He's got comments on everything from Genesis to Bethlehem, from Blue Bell to Shiner Bock. If you're a Texan (native or born again) you'll cotton to stories like Beach Blanket Bubba, Bubba at Deep Eddy, and Bubba at Dime Box - and you'll want to share him with your friends. (176pp.)

Books may be purchased at your local bookstore
or by using this form:

Stone Angel Books
P O Box 27392
Austin, Texas 78755-2392

Please send:

___ *Surviving Death* ($9.95)	$ _____
___ *God's Laughter* ($9.95)	_____
___ *The Eighth Day* ($8.95)	_____
___ *Gospel/Bubba* ($9.95)	_____

Texans (excluding Bubba) add 8% tax   _____

Postage/handling
    1 book/$1.25   _____
    2 books/$2.00   _____
    3 books/$3.00   _____
    4 books/FREE   _____

TOTAL $ _____

Make check or Money Order payable to

Stone Angel Books

Name _____

Address _____

City _____ State _____ Zip _____

(Want books autographed? Indicate "to whom".)